Also by Michael Ballé and Freddy Ballé
The Gold Mine
The Lean Manager

LEAD WITH RESPECT

a novel of **lean practice**

by

Michael Ballé *&* Freddy Ballé

Foreword by Jim Womack

Published by the Lean Enterprise Institute

Lean Enterprise Institute

Design: Thomas Skehan, Off-Piste Design
Library of Congress Control Number: 2014943619
ISBN: 978-1-934109-47-2.

This book is a work of fiction. Names, characters, businesses, organizations,
places, events, and incidents either are the product of authors' imaginations or
are used fictitiously. Any resemblance to actual persons (living or dead), events,
or locations is coincidental.

Lean Enterprise Institute, Inc.
215 First Street, Suite 300
Cambridge, MA 02142
617-871-2900 • fax: 617-871-2999 • lean.org

For Roman and Alexandre

FOREWORD

Lead with Respect is the third volume in a remarkable series of books by Michael and Freddy Ballé. In their first volume, *The Gold Mine*, the authors provided an enormous amount of practical guidance about the application of lean tools, inside a story of business transformation. In the second volume, *The Lean Manager*, the authors described a complete system of lean management inside a second story of business transformation.

In this third volume, the authors turn to the topic of lean leadership and demonstrate the essential behaviors of a transformational lean leader. The key behavior is to *lead with respect* by developing the problem-solving skills of everyone at every level of the organization. This begins with Southcape Software CEO Jane Delaney, who transforms herself—with the coaching of Andrew Ward, the European VP of her company's prime customer—by going to her company's gemba to see the real issues, challenge the current situation, and teach everyone problem solving so the whole organization can learn. As Andrew says to Jane at the outset, "The problem is you," and she responds with a journey of personal transformation told inside a third story of business transformation, at Southcape Software.

For readers encountering the Ballés (father Freddy and son Michael) for the first time, I welcome you to a world of struggle and great difficulties but, as always, with an eventual happy ending as the transformed Southcape not only survives but flourishes. For readers who started with *The Gold Mine* or *The Lean Manager*, I'm happy to report that Bob Woods, Phil Jenkinson, and Andrew Ward are alive and well, and still teaching core lean concepts and coaching leader behaviors, transmitted through rapid generations—from Bob's original teachers from Toyota in Japan to Phil to Andrew and now to Jane

Delaney. This mirrors the cascaded teaching and coaching process many of us in the Lean Community have been involved in—as pupils first and then teachers—for more than 30 years as lean concepts and practices have diffused across the world and through every value-creating activity.

The great thing about the Ballé books is that you can read them as prequels or sequels in any order and still derive the same knowledge and inspiration. Plus they are fun!

Of course, you then need to turn this knowledge into sustainable, standard behaviors, beginning with your own as a leader who develops your people by leading with respect. This skill is only gained through practice and will unavoidably involve many struggles with difficult problems as you join the long march of lean practitioners through the generations. The Ballé books are a great way to get started or to speed up your pace of transformation, personal and organizational. So I wish you the best of luck—in the good company of Andrew and Jane—as you pursue your continuing lean journey.

– Jim Womack
 Barter's Island, ME
 July 2014

Chapter One

LEAD FROM THE GROUND UP

Jane Delaney could take no more.

"Enough!" the CEO of Southcape Software told the representatives of Nexplas, her key client. "Enough. Do you understand how hard we have worked for you on this project? And how much we've delivered? And yet all you've done today is pick at problems and criticize our work. You show us no respect."

Making an effort to show support for her team, she gathered herself and continued, "I realize you're my customer, but our company will *not* be treated this way. We will fix the issue. At Southcape we always deliver for our customers. We simply need a little more time."

Andrew Ward, VP of Nexplas, fixed his gaze on her intently. They had been working on this project for six months now and had yet to complete the first key milestone. Unless things changed dramatically—and immediately—both the project and the entire relationship would unravel. They had to talk.

"Jane," he said, firmly, "we do have a problem. And I do not think we are going to solve it here in this meeting. Can we talk in your office?"

———

The two of them stood facing each other over her desk.

"The problem is *you*," Ward said.

"What—" Delaney blurted out before biting off the rest of her response. He was the client and this business was not going well but ... well, *really*?

"What do you mean by that, exactly?" she started again.

"The problem is you," Ward repeated, with a calmness that exasperated her.

"After all the lecturing on developing partnerships with your suppliers, now, now you shift the blame to us?" said Delaney, who caught herself and added, "We may have communication difficulties, but in my world communication is a two-way street."

"I didn't mean you as in your company," he corrected her. "I mean *you*, personally. You're the senior manager here."

She glared back at him, incredulous.

He looked at her openly and said, "As execs, it's *our* job to make sure our people succeed. They have a right to succeed, not an obligation. And this creates clear obligations for us as managers— as bosses. We need to understand the details of their work to help them overcome all the obstacles that stop them from doing a good job: the safety issues, the overburden, the bad organization, the faulty material, the poor work methods, and so on. That's *our* job."

"What makes you—"

"Look, I believe that *you* need to figure out what the client wants. *You* need to understand what your teams do every day. All so that *you* can help them succeed—and we can finally work together in a more constructive manner."

He paused while she simmered, furious at being lectured. She resisted a quick response, all too aware that as a successful woman she was always in danger of being judged as too harsh or too emotional. She hunkered down in her chair and fixed an impassive stare on him.

"Please, I realize it's hard to hear. I am sorry, but I need to say this," he continued. "I came here to see what was going on and after the session we've both witnessed I am ready to pull the plug on the entire project. Which is what my procurement manager has advised.

You'll agree that this was more of a wrestling match than a productive meeting, and quite frankly, our commitment to value-creating work does not allow us such waste."

"But—"

"However," he cautioned, "because this project is critical for us, and in the spirit of making every effort to understand each other, I've asked to have a word with you in private, and I'm standing here trying to get through to you. The question is: are you listening?"

She resented his arrogance, chalking up some of it to his survival skills in the world of automotive bullies. Truth is, as she checked her anger, she had to admit he wasn't being that overbearing. Direct to the point of rudeness maybe, condescending, probably, but now he stood quietly, looking at his shoes, as if *he* were embarrassed.

Damn, they looked so young these days. She'd bet he was hardly 40, a tall thin guy with receding black hair and bags under his clear blue eyes. He was the European VP of Nexplas, a large automotive supplier, and had made the effort to visit their offices. This was unusual in itself—she usually dealt with IT people, rarely with the top dogs themselves.

Heaven knew Southcape couldn't afford to lose yet another contract. You can do this, she told herself. Save face, save the contract.

"What do you mean, the problem is *me*, personally?" she asked with a less combative tone. "I've only been involved in this project since Peter Rodriguez left the company and left us all in a lurch."

"Well, that is part of the problem, and why we'd like to make an effort to continue working with you guys—we enjoyed working with Peter and by all accounts he did a terrific job for us. In fact, he gave us advance notice that he was looking for another job because he couldn't stand working for Southcape any more."

"He did what?" she started. "He went behind my back … and told you that he quit because of me? That's—"

"Not you, specifically," he interrupted.

"Then what—"

"Yes, we knew what was happening and did nothing about it—that's on us. We have certainly not done our best to continue the partnership, which is why we're having this difficult conversation now." He pressed on, with a distant look that gave the impression he was not entirely comfortable with his message. "But you're the CEO. That's what I'm trying to tell you. It all comes down to *you*."

"What? Forgive me, but we've been dealing with shifting and rarely explicit expectations—not to mention resistance to the things that we know we do well! And now you're saying that it's *my* fault!" she said, wondering if she was going too far in defending the company by citing her complaints with Nexplas.

"Yep," he answered coolly. "And I know the feeling—my CEO told me the same thing a long time ago, and I took it really badly. How could I be the problem, right? Nothing else was working!

"Please let me try to explain. In many ways this all comes down to respect, as you said. Respect is a practice that has many important meanings for us at Nexplas. Our main strategy is to develop the company through the development of its human resources. We have a general phrase for this: *lead with respect.*

"Our core belief is achieving our objectives through developing people. *Lead with respect* is a practice, mind you—a number of actions and approaches that enable us to realize this as something we do, rather than something we merely say.

"We *respect* people's experience and creativity, and their right to feel safe and succeed at what they do: customers, employees, and suppliers." He ticked off several points on his fingers as he spoke.
- We *engage* everybody all the time in problem solving, together, by making every effort to understand each other's point of view.
- This guarantees *quality, productivity,* and *flexibility* as we try to eliminate nonsatisfaction and nonvalue-added work. At the end of the day, productivity is wealth.

- We *share success* and *reward involvement and initiative,*
which makes our respect promise credible and sustains
our long-term growth. Customer satisfaction simply can't
happen without employee satisfaction.

"And that's it," he said, staring at his open hand reflectively.
"Lord knows we don't always succeed, but we struggle to follow this
practice every day. This is never easy and it never happens on its own.
It's a tough slog—especially for the CEO who must lead this. That
said, it's essential, and if you can't understand what we mean by *lead
with respect,* I doubt that we can continue to work together.

"Let me backtrack," he said, leaning back against the wall.
"Partnerships are very important to us, but not on any terms. We look
at every business situation as both *results and relationships.* We try to
be clear on what we seek from both. Results are clear, measurable
goalposts, whether financials or operational. We all know about that."

She nodded, tight-lipped.

"But we also understand that sustainable results can be achieved
only within stable relationships based on mutual trust. We've found
that results are an outcome of step-by-step improvement, which can
only happen within strong relationships, which involves a
commitment on both sides to make the partnership work. Attitude is
key and the first step is a genuine effort to understand each other."

"Amen to that," she quipped at his sermon. "But shouldn't you
practice what you've been preaching to me? How can you speak so
highly of respect when your company's reputation is based on its
mastery of *lean?*"

"So?" he asked, taken aback.

"So?" she repeated. "We all know what reputation lean has:
relentless productivity gains, management by pressure, people working
until they drop. Grinding suppliers into the ground. Scraping up
pennies where you can find them … I'll be damned if I let Nexplas
use any cultish program to justify such ghastly methods."

Now it was Ward's turn to be exasperated. "Yes, lean is the mainstay of our strategy," he replied, edgily, "and lean is why we grow twice as fast and twice as profitably as our competitors. And it has nothing do with any of those rumors you've heard.

"For us, lean means that we continuously strive to improve safety, quality, flexibility, and productivity by involving all employees in problem solving every day. Their initiatives and creativity guide us in growing the company and enhancing work.

"Lean is *not* about pressuring people, plain and simple. Actually, pressure isn't even the right word. Come to think of it, we do pressure people—but in a manner that we consider productive—what you might call healthy tension. That said, overburden is the first thing we strive against, and the safety of our employees—physically and morally—comes before anything else. And *we mean it.*

"And," he continued intently, "it matters not one whit that all the idiots out there call their Taylorist cost-cutting programs 'lean.' *This is not that.* Real lean is most emphatically not about making people work harder. We strive every day to make people work smarter. This is not the same thing at all. For us, lean is all about challenging yourself and each other to find the right problems, and working hard every day to engage people in solving them. So I don't know what you've heard about lean, but this is a good time to learn about what it really means. Lean is about kaizen and *respect!*"

"Respect!" she scoffed.

"Absolutely, *respect,*" he repeated earnestly, emphasizing the word. "Respect of every person's development to the full of their abilities, respect of every person's wish to succeed, and respect in doing our utmost to understand each other and solve problems together."

"Right," she said curtly. "Tell you what. Why don't you just say what you want from us."

"Here's the deal," he nodded, firmly. "I'm willing to continue this project if I have your *personal* commitment that we will build a partnership between my division and your company—on our terms.

If we can do that, there is a lot of potential work for you, because I have an urgent need to deploy this pilot in all the sites across the division."

"What do you mean, on your terms?"

"I'm willing to teach you to work differently, if you're willing to learn. Just like I've been taught myself."

"Teach me?" she asked, aghast.

"Yes. But you've got to commit to learn to work with us. You. Personally."

They sized each other up over a tense silence.

"I realize this is not how you thought this meeting would go," Ward finally said. "If it helps you feel any better, back when I was a plant manager it took me a long, long time to accept that I needed to learn before I could solve the plant's problems. All I ask at this stage is that you think over what I'm asking of you. If I don't hear from you within the week, we'll just leave it at that. Fair enough?"

She nodded, not trusting herself to speak, and composed herself as she steered him out of the room and back to the lobby where the Nexplas people and her own team were exchanging angry stares, equally impatient to go their separate ways. Partnership indeed!

———

Ward sighed deeply as he climbed into his taxi. He was of two minds about the meeting. On the one hand, the altercation was a disappointment to him—yet another reminder that doing the right thing often felt in the moment quite the opposite. He felt bad for putting Jane Delaney on the spot like this. She had looked really annoyed. On the other hand, he was pleased that he'd managed to confront her—albeit inelegantly. He was working hard on balancing how direct he should be in his position, and his occasional discomfort with this meant that when he did face up to difficult issues he often appeared overbearing, even if it was a defensive attitude. But he had been challenged to address this situation by his CEO Phil Jenkinson, so he was glad that at least he tried.

After years of being coached by Phil, he felt comfortable with the lead with respect management model when it came to managing his own troops. He had eventually codified the model into seven steps:

1. *Go and see* is a foundation of lean practice—the idea that all work takes place within a context, and that people (not processes, systems, or organization) make results. Go and see is about leading from the front by seeing the actual situation, and meeting with people one-by-one to learn, challenge, and support.

2. *Challenge* is about giving a clear direction and defining success in terms of progress or improvement goals. Rather than telling people what to do, challenge is about leading them to agree on a clear description of the problem, the criteria for an acceptable solution, and the expected pace of progress.

3. *Listen* means understanding the barriers people saw in their way to reaching the challenge, seeing the obstacles they had to overcome through their eyes, and empathizing with their moments of discouragement in the face of what could seem like steep adversity. Understanding doesn't mean agreeing; it's an essential foundation for any constructive relationship.

4. *Teach problem solving* is about developing his staff's autonomy to analyze and solve their own problems. This often means giving them a hard time on correctly visualizing the problem and seeking root causes before jumping to the first obvious solution. This requires day-in, day-out, hands-on coaching. Most importantly, this means giving people space to think for themselves.

5. *Support* by both engaging and involving people in their own workplace. Engaging people means encouraging them to feel responsible for the problems they encounter and support them in trying out new ideas, even if these could lead to failure.

(Hopefully, the problem-solving coaching would limit the number of really bad ideas.) Involving is about recognizing improvement efforts and making sure people feel ownership for their ideas when they're implemented, so that they can see their contributions to the company as a whole.

6. *Teamwork* is about developing people's individual skill in working with each other. Andy had come to see that he absolutely needs his employees to work across functional boundaries and that he can only foster teamwork by getting people with different outlooks to solve problems together.

7. *Learn* is the part of the model he was focusing on personally. As his staff solve problems and come up with unexpected initiatives and creative solutions, his understanding of what is and isn't possible changes. As he delves into the details of what they've done, some avenues for success close but others open. He was excited to discover that his understanding of the overall challenges deepens through the study of people's local initiatives.

Seven Practices of Lead with Respect

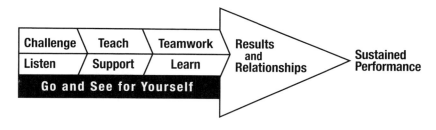

He thought of these steps as the *seven practices of lead with respect* that he carried out daily until they had became his own seven habits. With hindsight, he had found this practice to be surprisingly robust.

The hairy part was the constant need to find the correct balance between driving hard for results and listening hard to grow relationships, like a two-stroke engine.

Back when he was a plant manager, he often felt like he'd fallen in a ditch on both sides of the path. At first he overempathized with his staff to the point of running afoul of his own boss because of his poor results—in fact, he almost lost his job.

Then he overcompensated by becoming a petty tyrant, which delivered immediate results, but drove the plant workers to strike and almost cost him his job again. He was thankful that Jenkinson had been patient with him. He had taught him the balance between strong leadership (be clear on where you want to go) and empathy (listen to your people and understand their problems as they see it), between teaching rigorous problem solving (run this analysis again) and understanding the human need for approval and validation.

Getting people to open up to a new kind of thinking was always a case of "damned if you do, damned if you don't." He knew that he had to be direct to get their attention, but he had enough battle scars to know that if their ego got too badly bruised, he'd never get beyond the first step. He had learned repeatedly that respect—and lean itself—was not something he could explain just by talking the talk; people needed to walk the walk. Understanding this system could only come through experience. All the best books, resources, and workshops were table stakes compared to learning through actual practice.

Reflecting on his scene at Southcape with Jane Delaney, he wondered whether he should have made a better case for lean. After all, he had learned from experience that lean worked, plain and simple. Nexplas was doing incredibly well. In the five years since Jenkinson had taken over the company, its value had multiplied four-fold. They had taken over another company and purchased additional plants, such as the Swindon site he was now trying to sort out. They were increasing their market share in a depressed market, and their profitability was twice that of any of their competitors.

Ward himself had done very well in this transformation, moving rapidly from plant manager to European VP. When he took the time to think about it, lean had made him wealthier than he'd ever thought he'd be. But that wasn't the issue.

Working for Jenkinson made sense—and sometimes was even *fun*. He had a management approach unlike any other top exec. He believed that people—not organizations or systems—delivered results. He would explain that top performance came from great people running great processes, and that people made the processes. He would never design solutions for himself and then look for people to implement his ideas. His strength was carefully developing people to enable them to figure out answers to business issues. He was not running the company with a few brains around him managing lots of pairs of hands. He challenged all the brains in the firm to move the business forward.

Ultimately, lean and respect were all about people, and not in some "soft" sentimental manner. To improve performance, Andy had to improve processes, and to improve processes he had to improve his people, their individual competencies and their ability to work with others. This was essentially how *lead with respect* delivered results. If your people are better at what they do, the processes they come up with can't be copied by the competition. Learning turns into competitive advantage because others can't copy you—they have to follow the same learning curve.

His challenge was how to teach others as he had been taught. He was completely sold on *lead with respect*, not from blind faith but firsthand experience. But getting others to see the brilliance of this approach remained a puzzle. An urgent puzzle at that, now that he had this massive business—including suppliers—to turnaround quickly. He questioned whether he had challenged Jane too much, but he didn't know any other way to get through to her. "They don't know what they don't know," he reminded himself, and they can't see what they don't know is there unless you make them look.

Jenkinson certainly had not spared him in their first discussions when he was a struggling plant manager. He remembered feeling both challenged and angry in their early talks. But he'd also found that, as soon as he'd started to *do* things rather than argue, Phil had been patient and understanding to a fault. And the company had evolved into a place where people could just say what they had in mind, and trust in the strength of the relationship.

As a VP now, he called it as he saw it. But with Southcape, he belatedly realized he was in a completely different situation. He had enough experience—both good and bad—to feel confident in how he managed people who reported to him. But in this case, his challenge was to convey the model to someone who not only did not report to him but, as Jane had intimated several times, didn't think she had anything to learn from him. She was an established CEO in her own right, and he'd treated her as if she'd been one of his employees. She'd probably take all he meant about respect *exactly* the wrong way, feeling he'd been disrespectful to her. He feared that he had pushed too hard on the challenge front, but that seemed inevitable at the outset … In any case, he didn't know what to do better to actually get people to listen up. But the risk was to offend them utterly and lose them.

"Oh, well," he finally told himself with a mental shrug, "stuff happens, move on!" He'd definitely have to work harder at figuring out how to get his suppliers on board. He'd be easier on her next time … if there was a next time.

———

Jane Delaney was wondering the same thing.

"The deal is dead, right?" asked Simon Burnsell, the project manager who had taken over from the rat Rodriguez when he'd left.

"Not quite," she sighed, keeping her face blank. "No thanks to you guys. That was some performance you've put on in there!"

"Oh, come on, be fair," jumped in Daniela Webb. "You've seen what they're like. If they already have all the answers, what do they need us for?"

"Their VP just told me that they were very happy with Peter's work," Delaney replied coldly.

"There we go again," Simon sighed.

"Yes," Delaney agreed. "Let's not have this discussion *again*. Did you guys reach any conclusions while I was talking to the head honcho?"

"They gave us an action plan," answered Daniela. "There's no real logic to it. Just a list of 'To Do' points."

"Okay, team, we'll look at that in the morning—let's call it a day," Jane concluded. "Let's all go home and think on this. It's not off yet, but close. Remember, losing Nexplas would be a real setback, so I expect some soul searching from all of you tonight. Remember, team, I really am counting on you—you can do it."

––––––––––

Naturally, Jane got caught in the heavy traffic of rush hour by driving home early. She fumed as she inched her way along the familiar route, thinking that there was at least one upside to usually returning late from work.

She was angry: at the traffic, her team, and most of all, that arrogant Andy Ward. The worst of it was that he'd touched a nerve. Two years ago, when Southcape Software's founder and sole owner David Marais, had decided to sell and go back to his native South Africa (bless him), the three senior directors had pooled together and found a private equity firm to set up a leveraged buyout. She took the President and CEO role while Rob "bloody" Taylor became Sales VP and Mike Wembley chief technologist. She'd had many doubts then, but never, never in a hundred years would she have thought she might fail. After all, she'd been all but running the company in the last years of David's tenure, particularly as he became embroiled in his third—and nastiest—divorce, which in the end had sent him scuttling back to whatever Afrikaans farm he'd come from.

She smiled grimly to herself thinking that she missed the old rogue. Since he'd left, it had been nothing but bad luck and trouble. The economy was sputtering along with nary a recovery in sight, the software world had become worse than cutthroat, and the blood-sucking shareholders and bankers wanted their pound of flesh every month. Every month!

She just didn't understand why it was all so hard. The company was well established. They had several massive projects in banking where they originally started, then pharmaceuticals, and more recently manufacturing and warehousing. The people were not brilliant, but they were sound. They were a bit on the expensive side, maybe. But overall, clients had seemed satisfied.

She still couldn't get her head around why she had lost so many large contracts since David left. Rob was still selling, but it seemed that every new gig was harder, meaner, and profitability was dropping fast. If she didn't find a way to turn things around, she would be unable to pay the bankers soon—and if she broke the covenants, then real hell would break lose. And now the Nexplas project.

––––––––––

Jane cursed as she struggled to open her front door, reminding herself to fix the lock. Her younger daughter Marie was sprawled on the rug in front of the TV doing her homework with her tiny speakers on and books and magazines spread all around the floor. This drove Jane crazy, as usual, but she managed to blow her daughter a kiss without telling her off.

"Hi, Mom," she said, barely looking up. "Sara is upstairs. She's staying home tonight."

Sara, her oldest, was in her first year of college and supposedly living in the dorm. Something must have happened—another crisis to deal with probably.

Suddenly it was just too much. She walked straight through the open kitchen and out into their tiny garden without even taking the time to drop her handbag. A strong wind was blowing and the winter stars were shining crisp and cold. She dove into her bag and brought out the pack of smokes she'd guiltily bought earlier in the week.

Time—she needed time. Time to think. Time to sort herself out. Time to figure out what was happening to the business. Time to take better care of her kids. Time to—

"Mom? Do you smell this? It smells like cigarettes ... Oh, Mom! You promised!"

"They just don't get it," said Simon in his quiet voice, the following morning. He was their most experienced project manager and knew his way around operational software thoroughly. Over the years, Jane had come to realize that his flat tone and mild manner could conceal how opinionated he really was—particularly about technical issues.

"Go on," she asked.

"For starters, their ERP is completely crap. It's something out of the dark ages. It's slow, the user interface is confusing as hell, their data structure is incoherent and a nightmare to work with, the system is unstable and buggy, and there's something wrong with their server connection. As a result the system often crashes."

"Yeah, and they have a runaway modular approach. Every department builds their own bits and bobs—none of them integrate well with each other," added Chris Williamson. His T-shirt read *I don't have an attitude problem, you have a perception problem.* Topical as well as typical, Jane thought wryly.

"We understand what they want to do fairly well and it's a radical move," Simon continued. "But it can't be done without cleaning up their existing data structure first."

"Which they adamantly refuse to look into," added Sharon Miller, their graphics expert. "They won't even question their data entry screens!"

"Typical resistance to change," chipped in Daniela, never short of useful insights.

Ryan Cox, the last developer/tester on the team, remained quiet as usual, looking at them thoughtfully behind thick glasses—as if *they* were the odd specimens in the jar. The kid was really good at cracking code, but had the personal appeal of a slug.

"What about this action plan?" Jane asked. "Let's have it. What's on the top of the list?"

"Spending more time at the production site," snorted Daniela, shaking her long black curls in annoyance. "It's all the way by Swindon—over a hundred miles away. Just getting there and back takes an entire day."

"We're late enough as it is," agreed Chris. "And it's not like it's our only project."

"Simon?"

"I agree. We've wasted enough time there already. Our real problem is how to educate them into understanding that what they are asking for simply won't get them where they want to go."

"Which is?" she asked.

"Well, it's tricky. They'd like to change the entire logic of the materials requirement planning for their procurement, from inventory control to lead-time tracking. It's a massive project."

"What was Peter doing with them that they were so pleased with?"

"You know Peter. Nifty pieces of shoddy code here and there."

"Bits and bobs? Like what they do themselves?"

"Absolutely. One thing they really liked is that they were building a supplier list per part in a spreadsheet—a spreadsheet can you believe it? Peter managed to code a module that they could access from the main interface, nothing more. Stuff like that. All the users over there complain how full of holes it is, but the bosses simply don't care."

"And so far, they've rejected all our proposals?"

The team fell silent as she looked at each of them in turn.

"Okay," she sighed. "Item two on their wish list."

"Fix all the bugs that Peter left behind," snickered Chris.

"Now that's rich," snorted Daniela.

"That's what they asked for," confirmed Simon, speaking so softly it was almost a whisper. Jane had long suspected that the low voice affectation was a strategy to force others to listen, on a par with his black Steve Jobs turtlenecks and black pants, an outfit that never quite looked right with his nondescript face crowned with his remaining patches of brown hair around his ears.

"That's not unreasonable," she said. "It would give us a good place to start off again and get to grips with whatever Peter was doing with them."

No one answered. They wouldn't meet her eye again. What was going on?

"They said they wouldn't pay for it," Simon told her when the pause became awkward.

"Fine," she stated. She needed a smoke so bad she could taste it. "So they're pissed, and they want us to show that we're willing. Need I remind you this is a really big client and we need this to succeed? We'll make a commercial gesture."

"You'd better talk to Rob about this," rasped Simon, still not looking at her.

"Okay, I will. Now, let's get cracking, let's do it."

Still no reaction from the team around the table, apart from Ryan's superior smirk.

"What else?" she asked.

"You know Peter!" exclaimed Daniela, dark eyes flashing.

"You keep saying that. What about Peter?"

"He did everything on his own, did his own testing, this so-called 'agile' stuff he kept going on about. He automated his tests as he went by writing his code."

"Like it worked," snorted Simon. "We all know how full of bugs his code always was."

"And?" Delaney asked impatiently.

"Well… we've got the code, but—"

"But… what?"

"None of us really understand what he did. There's a lot of strange logic in there, and we'll need to spend a long time just figuring it out. Typical Peter."

"As if yours was easier to understand," fired Daniela, turning unexpectedly on Simon. "That last piece of code you sent for testing was just awful."

"So, the good news is that you eventually got around to look at it, right?" he retorted.

"What is that supposed to mean?"

"Oh, come on now, Daniela," dove in Chris. "You're so busy with the MRX project you're not pulling your weight on Nexplas!"

"I beg your pardon? You should see the rate at which your builds fail. It's not testing anymore, it's rewriting! …"

———————

Delaney watched the meeting degenerate into bickering and name-calling. This was supposed to be a team? Was this accidental? Or a true reflection of what the entire company was turning into? She felt that morale was low and that conflict had risen over the past year, but she dismissed it as an unavoidable consequence of tough times out there. Could there be more to it?

This was the first time in a good long while she had actually sat with a team. She'd been so busy managing the business, dealing with clients, and generally running "important" things that her interaction had mostly been with project managers at the weekly staff meeting. Watching them squabble like this was painful. This was exactly the kind of infighting that had driven the car guys nuts at the meeting yesterday. Worst of all, she realized that she did not have an idea about what the issues really were anymore. She could not remember the last time she had actually looked at any of their code.

Then it suddenly hit her: this was not about software. She had been so angry with Ward for presuming that he could teach her something when he clearly didn't know a thing about software. But as she took a hard look at her team arguing with each other, she realized this *was* about management, not IT. Her management.

The team was being dysfunctional in the exact way she remembered from her first jobs in banking. That was why she moved to coding and then joined David's start-up gamble! It made her feel sick to see that her company had become the run-of-the-mill outfit she had despised and fled.

It hurt to admit it, but Ward might have been right: it was about her and her management style. She might have to face up to that, and to the consequences this might have for Southcape as a whole. What was it that he had said about respect? She'd been so angry she couldn't even remember the few points he had made repeatedly. She needed to wrap up the meeting and think about this—not as an IT Director, but as the CEO of any business.

"Enough!" she said firmly. "Listen to yourselves. Is this how we want to work? Is this who we want to be?"

Her employees were so taken up with their arguments that none of them even appeared embarrassed by all of this. She stared at a silent group of sullen faces.

"We're going to do exactly what we've been told to do by Nexplas," she said evenly. "End of story. Yesterday their VP told me that the action plan is not about the software. The action plan is really a test of our commitment to work with them."

"But—" started Chris.

"No buts, no ifs," she cut him off. "Simon, you're going to get your team to put together an item-by-item plan of how we will follow what Nexplas has asked us to do, and we'll review this at the end of today. That's all there is to it. Now let's get to *work*!" she said, standing briskly and leaving the room.

———————

That evening, after giving up on getting her daughter to talk about why she chose to drive an hour back to sleep at home rather than stay in her dorm—and dismissing for the moment the usual motherly worries about sex, drugs, and rock and roll—she gnawed on another bone.

What could she possibly have missed about David's departure? Hell, he had already practically left the running of the company to her. Everyone at the director level had recognized her chops, which made her as the obvious choice for CEO when he left.

What had David been doing that she was not? He had been looking at the code. That's what. In the last couple of years, he was rarely at the office, that's true. Too busy with his personal troubles at home and, as she gathered, falling madly in love for some young chick—a man at his age! All the business decisions came to her. But when he was in, he sat with the teams reviewing their code. She could suddenly picture him, looking half asleep under his mop of gray hair, old-fashioned tie askew, balanced back in his chair, feet on the table as the team projected their code on the screen and he questioned how they went about it line-by-line.

David had a degree in operational research from Cape Town University, back when there was still a Soviet Union and a wall divided the world between the free and the Reds. He joined the IT department of a major U.K. bank, and led the charge in minicomputers. (Mini-computers, do any of these kids even know what they were?)

In the final wild yuppie years of the eighties, he jumped on the outsourcing bandwagon to exploit the possibilities of desktop computing. He created Southcape Software with Jeremy Nicks, another old-timer, and had taken Jane, Rob, and Mike Wembley along. He quickly bought Jeremy out and become sole owner. The four of them coded night and day for little pay, but it had been fun. They expanded out of the banking industry and grew the company to its current size.

David had been an indifferent administrator, but the man was a charmer, and never lost his childish delight at solving complex problems with clever bits of code. He hated all the "quality" stuff that had come to dominate the industry. He never tired of ranting against best practices and qualification systems. "Great people make great software," he would repeat as a mantra.

"Walking the code," he called it. He'd shuffle into the office, grab a cup of coffee, and chat with whoever was there. Then he would stroll into any project room apparently at random, interrupt the work, and ask the team to gather together and show him code—what could they say, he was the boss, wasn't he?

She hadn't done that in forever. She had rushed on with the job of setting up the deals and keeping the company together. And then she kept on doing the type of work that she knew she did exceptionally well—and told herself that her competence in this area translated into effective leadership. But—it hit her like a ton of bricks—she had lost touch with what they were doing. She hadn't participated in one code review over the past two years. She didn't know the company's products anymore.

Could that be the root of the problem? Could the problem really be her? It seemed unlikely that she was the source of the disarray she was currently witnessing—but still, the doubt was nagging.

———

"Ward speaking."

"Andrew. Hi. It's Jane Delaney from Southcape. Is this a good time to speak?"

"Jane, sure, hang on, I'll get out of this, wait a sec—"

She heard production noises in the background and then quiet.

"That's better, go ahead."

"Okay. Assuming the problem is *me* …"

"Ah. That," Ward replied calmly. "I probably came off as direct—perhaps too much so? I hope that I didn't come down too hard …"

"Don't worry. You certainly made me think. I've been wondering. Maybe you're right, maybe the problem is me. The question is: where do I go from here?"

"Um. Have you gone through the action plan with your team?"

"Yes. We'll do it."

"Great—well, that's all there is to it, really."

"You said you could teach me."

"Ah, did I?"

"You said your CEO taught you."

"That he did," Andy chuckled. "And it wasn't pretty. I almost got my plant closed down before I accepted that I needed to learn."

"I'd like to take you at your word. I need to learn and fast. So, can you teach me?"

There was a long silence on the phone. She suddenly feared that she'd pushed too hard. She was going out on a limb here and might have just sabotaged the contract if this guy reacted the wrong way. She resisted the urge to say something and counted seconds in her head.

"I don't know," he finally said. "I can try, if you're sure that's what you want."

"It is. Where do we start?"

"Um, well—the action plan is a good place to start. Look, we purchased this Swindon site a year ago and I'm spending a lot of time here integrating it with the rest of the division. Let's find a time when I'm in the plant and I can show you around."

"How would that help me?" she blurted out. "What does a production plant have to do with a software house?"

"Go and see," he told her. "First lesson, and probably last lesson. If I had a dime for every time my CEO has asked me 'have you seen it yourself?' I'd be a rich man by now. 'Stop, look, and listen,' he says. The main problem your team has right now is that you don't understand us. Which means you don't know how to lead them to understand us. *Lead with respect* starts with go and see, and finding the facts for yourself at the source."

"Okay. Go and see—what?"

"The real place, where value is created. It's what we call the gemba in lean lingo. It's where customers work, where your own teams work, and where suppliers work. Real place, real products, real people, real relationships—that's what we look at."

"Is that why you came to visit us, rather than have us meet you at the plant?"

"Yes, I needed to see your workplace for myself."

"But there's nothing to see at Southcape, we do software. It's all in the computers!"

"Precisely!" he laughed.

"Go and see," she repeated doubtfully. "And then what?"

"Ah," he hesitated. "I guess I'm not going at this right. Let's take a step back and see if I can explain.

"I'm talking about respect. The management method that I'm learning from my boss is based on a specific form of respect. He calls it, *lead with respect*. He doesn't mean respect in the common sense of being polite, but respect in the deeper sense of relating to our customers, employees, and other stakeholders. It's respect for the development of the autonomy of every person. *Lead with respect* is not a theory, it's a *practice*—or several practices, I should say. It's not something you learn by reading a book or by analysis. It's something you learn through practice every day, and blimey, it's hard."

"Right," she said, doubtfully.

"Yeah, I know, it takes a while to buy into, but that's the basic deal. I can show you the practice, but then you've got to, um, practice. There's no way around it. And the first practice is to go and see."

"Like walking the code?" she mused out loud.

"Walking the code?"

"Sorry, yes, reviewing code, line-by-line."

"Right. Absolutely, reviewing code, not to correct the work—that's the coder's responsibility—but to see how well people understand what they're trying to achieve, the problems they're trying to solve, and how well they work with each other."

"Hmm."

"Yes, well, I doubt we can do this on the phone. Come around to the plant and I'll try to explain. The main idea behind go and see is that you need to find the facts to make correct decisions and to build consensus about how to achieve your mutual goals. We need to get people to agree to what the problems are before we have them arguing about solutions. I'll have a go at showing you how we do this—not that we're brilliant at it, but we do try hard."

"In the plant then," she agreed, wondering what she was getting herself into.

"Sure. It's not that far, a couple of hours drive, no more."

"Yes. Not far."

"And, oh, bring your safety shoes."

"Safety shoes, right," she replied flatly. Was he pulling her leg?

Chapter Two

ALIGN SUCCESS
WITH VALUE

Safety shoes! Although Delaney had ignored Ward's comment, she had the good sense to wear sensible flats rather than her familiar heels. Even so, as she followed Ward with safety toe guards strapped on, she felt like Bozo the Clown. The fluorescent orange safety vest added to her awkwardness. She had abandoned her customary shawl and was feeling naked without it. Years ago, when she replaced her Bohemian clothes with business suits, she held on to a collection of brightly woven shawls and scarves as a statement of the flower child she had once been.

She had not visited a production site in a while, and thought to herself that the big machines spewing smelly plastic parts were grimy. Ward had popped his head into the project meeting with her and Simon and Chris and suggested he show her around. They exchanged pleasantries as he guided her across the plant toward the shipping dock. Shipping dock? What on earth was she supposed to learn there?

They entered a cavernous hall with huge stacks of large metal crates in neat rows reaching to the sky, and large forklifts zooming back and forth, loading waiting trucks.

"Watch out," said Ward. "Forklifts are supposed to stop for pedestrians but they don't always see us. Stick carefully to the painted walkways. We're creating no-go zones to separate machines from people, but it's not complete yet."

She nodded silently, curious about when (if?) he would tie this work to hers.

"Actually," Ward continued, looking around, "safety was my first battle here. The first challenge from my CEO when we purchased the plant was to cut accidents by half in the first year—people don't come to work to get hurt. This place had a dismal record on safety, and the attitude was that it was an operator problem, not a management issue.

"When I told them that safety was my number one priority, the unions jumped on it and said we should have 'safety first' as the first statement of our mission. It's hard to disagree with, but if we want this plant to have a future, our first duty is to our customers. Quality has to come first. So we wrangled and in the end came up with *quality first, safety always.* This sums up much of what *lead with respect* is after."

"I hear what you're saying on quality," protested Delaney, "but I can't quite see how safety could be an issue with Southcape. We don't have any of this ..." she waved her arm toward a passing forklift.

"Don't you?" he replied, amused. "Don't you get headaches? Backaches? Burnouts? Any work-related injury is a safety issue."

"If you look at it this way," she conceded, thinking back at how this indeed happened. "I see what you mean."

"The key to satisfied customers is satisfied employees," he insisted, as he started walking again with Delaney trailing after him. "And employees will never feel satisfied if they are ill or injured or don't feel safe at work. I have to admit it's a daily struggle. Every accident is reported immediately to me, and I expect an in-depth analysis within 24 hours. They're starting to understand that unsafe conditions can't be tolerated—although I had to stop production on the spot a few times before they got that. Now I'm trying to get them to focus on actual unsafe movements in people's jobs, but that's still a stretch.

"Ah, here we are," he said, gesturing toward an open area with a large whiteboard and a couple of flipcharts. "Safety is of course a prerequisite to success," he said. "But our first core belief about *lead with respect* is that *people have a right to succeed.*"

He paused for dramatic effect.

"I thought it was go and see the real place?"

"Um, yes," he said, nonplussed. "Yes, go and see the gemba is definitely the first step, you're right. In any case, people have a right to succeed and—"

"Surely you mean a duty to succeed?"

"Nope," he smiled, shaking his head. "That's the point. It's a right. People come to work to succeed. It's our responsibility as managers to support them so that they do. Every person has the right to succeed every time they do their job, and they also have the right to have a successful career."

"Wow. That's quite a statement."

"Yes, and in order to succeed they need to align their personal success with the value the customer expects. It's a high goal and we often fall short," he admitted. "But it works for us because we've realized that motivation comes from success, not the other way around. When people feel successful in their job, they're motivated to come to work and give it their best. What I've learned the hard way, is that in many cases employees can't succeed because of the side-effect of some policy I've instituted, never realizing all the consequences."

"Are you saying that you are the problem?" she quipped, suddenly seeing the humor in it.

"Absolutely," he grinned. "You're getting the drift. I'm the problem and so is my management team. Employees rarely are—they just want to get on with doing their job well. And yet we invent so many hurdles for them to overcome … how can they possibly succeed?"

As Ward slowed down to gather his thoughts, he steered Delaney to a bare table and sat down to explain.

"In order to succeed," he continued, "we have to agree on what success means for every job. Which means understanding what the customer values at every workstation. And by customer we mean both the final customer and the next person in the chain. And that's not the easiest part. To define success, we have to create metrics that really matter. We need to find some way of scoring the goals and counting fouls. Working in most environments is like being asked to run faster in a football match where the score is kept hidden and there's no referee to hand out red cards."

Delaney nodded, thinking back to what David had done in the company. Certainly he'd called out fouls in a way she'd never done.

"Phil Jenkinson—that's my CEO—bought this company because he likes the products which complement our range well. Unfortunately for them but fortunately for us, their operations were hopeless. They were essentially trying to optimize their asset use with the IT system, without any notion of the overall flow or real productivity. As a result their profitability was low and their cash situation was lousy. He thinks he got a bargain price as well as an 'in' to new customers. Now it's my job to sort out their operations without pissing off the few smart guys in engineering who design products."

"Um," Delaney nodded again, not quite sure how to respond.

"Ahh ...," he sighed, rubbing his face abstractedly. "'Moan and groan don't get the job done,' my pa always says. The long and the short of it is that the previous owners had no idea what success for operations meant."

"Operating at a profit?"

"Precisely not," grinned Ward. "Profitability is a result, the outcome of what we do, of all that we do. Focusing exclusively on financial results is like trying to drive a car by looking in the rearview mirror. So that's not what we focus on—in fact we've learned that doing so is dead wrong. Financial numbers are generated by the physical performance of our operations. It's the physical performance you've got to improve to see your financial numbers get better."

"You've lost me there," she confessed, puzzled.

"This is a factory, right?" he said, pointing at the production hall. "What is a factory supposed to do?"

"Build stuff?"

"Nope …" He paused for a beat. "Ship stuff! Good stuff, of course —the right stuff. This may seem like a fine distinction, but it makes all the difference in the world. And it matters regardless of what you make or do.

"You've got to look at your work from your customers' perspective: what do *they* value? What they want is good products delivered on time. So what we've got to do is pack good products into the right boxes, put the right boxes onto the right trucks, and ship them out on time. That's about it."

"Okay, that sounds fairly simple," she frowned. "I don't know much about factories, but weren't they doing that before?"

"They were shipping what they produced. But they never worried about whether they were shipping on time. They felt that 97% overall On-Time Delivery was good enough. They were completely missing the point."

"Ninety-seven percent on time isn't good enough?" she exclaimed.

"For automotive, no. For us, 97% OTD means 30,000 missed deliveries per million. That's appalling. The point is we aim for perfect delivery—although we'll probably never get there."

––––––––––

Ward spotted a short pudgy man with close-cropped hair walking by and he took Delaney over to meet him.

"Tim, great to see you. How are you doing today?"

"Not too bad, guv, not too bad."

Tim Russon spoke with a thick local accent. Delaney couldn't help notice that the overhanging neon light in the factory shone brightly off his balding pate.

"Tim, I'd like to ask for your help in sharing how we define success here. As dock manager, what does that mean to you?"

"Happy to help. By the way, you were right, it was too good to last," the man said, walking them over to a whiteboard.

Logistics whiteboard

Truck (client)	Depart date	Depart time	Prep zone	End of prep time	Status	Comments

At first sight, Jane found the board rather unimpressive, a large whiteboard that looked lost in this cavernous hall filled with huge metal containers stacked in neat rows almost to the ceiling and forklifts zipping to and fro. The whiteboard in fact looked a bit grubby, with barely legible comments scribbled over poorly erased previous ones. It was certainly a working tool, she conceded.

"Last time I was here they had had a perfect day," said Ward happily. "They shipped every truck 100% complete and on time."

"The guv here told us we'd got lucky, and we were, well, ticked off," said Tim, smiling wryly.

"They did a tremendous job, don't get me wrong," Ward said. "And the fact that they achieved 100% one day proved that it could be done. I was just warning them that they had stretched the rubber band far from where they originally were, and it was bound to pull back."

"That it did," Tim agreed.

"Reversal to the mean?" asked Jane, which earned her a surprised glance from Ward, who nodded, grinning encouragingly—or patronizingly, if she chose to look at it that way.

"Why don't you tell us how you got there?"

"Right. Well, when the guv first started visiting he told us we had to ship every truck complete and on time. We told him it wasn't possible because we don't control production and we don't control the delivery trucks. Customers use logistic companies, who send trucks to pick up loads, and they come more or less as and when they please. He said he wouldn't have any of it and asked us to track them using this graph." Tim showed her a tracking chart (*see page 32*).

"Then he asked us to set up this big board with a plan for every truck: departure date and time, preparation zone to find the parts, end of preparation time, status, and comments about what went wrong. We thought it was an absolute waste of time because, as I said, we don't control when the trucks arrive. But this was the new boss and I didn't want us to start on the wrong foot, so we did it."

"You did," agreed Ward sympathetically.

"And he was onto something. Just putting what we discovered up on the whiteboard helped us clarify what was happening. We could see that half the problem was getting parts from production, and half was that the customer trucks never arrive when they should. So now what? Well, this guy tells me that getting the trucks to show up on time was my responsibility. 'Bollocks,' I thought. How could I control customer trucks?"

Ward just stood there silently, inviting Tim to keep going.

"Talk to them, the guv says," Tim continued, with a nod toward Ward. "I didn't feel like it, but I did it. When the truck wasn't there on time, I called their dispatcher. The guv said, 'Don't tell them off, just ask them why they're not on time.' So I do as he says, and I hear all their life stories and so on. After a while, I find myself chatting to the same chaps over and over again. One of them turns out to be my wife's second cousin, believe it or not."

"And?" wondered Delaney, now intrigued.

"That's the magic part," he admitted. "We didn't do much more than fix small issues and talk more often, but pretty soon they were arriving on time more often. At the same time the guv was kicking the factory into delivering parts to us on time with all his kanban stuff. And then what do you know, one day we've got the right crates on hand, the right trucks are there, and we hit the 100% mark."

Logistics tracking chart

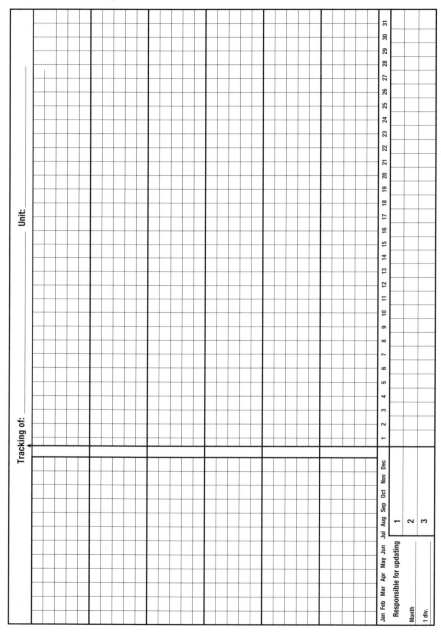

"Luck, as I said," Ward said, though he was clearly pleased. "I still took them out for curry. It was a good day."

"Right you are! Now we've got to figure out how to make it stick." Tim added.

"Are you saying you didn't change the computer system?" Jane asked, surprised. "To be honest, Andy, that's what I expected you wanted me to see."

"Nah," said Tim. "Our computer system is such a mess we wouldn't know what to change in the first place. I've got one guy full time just dealing with it. That's the first thing I told the guv—get us a new computer system and we'll deliver on time. 'But no go,' he said. 'Fix the relationship first, and then we'll see.'"

She looked askance at Ward—his man had just confirmed what her team kept telling her, but he looked back with a grin (patronizing? encouraging?) and said nothing.

"You improved delivery with these whiteboards?" she asked, dubious and curious at the same time. "Can I take pictures?" she asked, snapping the boards with her phone as Ward gave her a go-ahead sign.

"That's a yes. We didn't believe it then, but we do now," Tim concluded. "Sure the computer is a pain and we need to upgrade, but that's not what is driving our delivery performance. It's us."

––––––––

"You're telling me that you improved your delivery performance just by defining success?" asked Jane unconvinced, as they walked back toward the production area. They made their way through rows of large machinery that made loud mechanical sounds and generated a smell like burning tires.

"I'd say aligning success and value. And committing to kaizen."

"Kaizen?"

"Small step improvement. See, we don't start by making big changes. We support people in making small changes for the better every day. That's another part of showing respect. Tim knows that he truly owns the performance of the plant's delivery rate. That leads directly to improvement. Tim feels responsible for his delivery and he also knows that he is empowered to do something about it.

"If I'd changed the process, say, by upgrading the computer system right away, I'd never have gotten that. In fact, if I had swooped in and imposed large changes, that would have been disrespectful to him and may have done nothing to actually improve the situation. *Lead with respect* is about believing that every person can grow to better fulfill their job, if we all agree on what success is and determine the specific small steps we can make to improve creatively. I'm not saying we won't improve the IT. We just won't start there."

"And the boards?" Jane inquired, being careful not to push for a software upgrade and sound too sales-y.

"The boards are essential," explained Andy, pointing to another whiteboard in a production cell. "They visualize what we've defined collectively to be success. Again, they act like the scoreboard at a sports game. We see together, so we know together, so we can act together."

"But why the small steps?" she wondered. "Doesn't it take forever? Wouldn't a structural solution be quicker?"

"That's the trick," he smiled. "It took Tim and his team a year to get there, but get there they did. I could have done it differently, but never with this level of involvement; nor do I believe, with quite the same results.

"Look, I got really lucky with Tim. The production manager here is a much harder nut to crack. But that's kinda the point. As we worked on this specific project with Tim, two things happened. First, I managed to build some trust with the logistics team as they discovered what they could do themselves. And second, just as important, I managed to show the plant manager that small step improvements can lead to large changes. He was asking the same questions you are! It's always a struggle."

"I bet," she laughed suddenly.

"We need to understand change," he pursued. "Leading really is about getting people to change—their goals, their understanding, their attitude, their behavior, their competence. But you see, for any of us, change is partly exciting and partly scary. Agreed?"

She nodded.

"One reason managers get to be managers is that they find change more exciting than scary; they're always looking for the next magic bullet. To operators, change is scary, because they've learned the hard way that things never change for the better—at least not for them."

"Agreed."

"So, *lead with respect* is about understanding that change is scary and working as a manager to break down large challenges into small, everyday steps. The big change we introduce in how we work is helping everyone accept that day-to-day improvement is a normal part of the job. Jenkinson has defined it as:

$$JOB = WORK + KAIZEN$$

Andy wrote this on a piece of paper and stared for a moment at the three words, as if they were the key to something deeper. Then he said, "Doing the work is not enough. We're all expected to solve problems and suggest small step improvements every day. All of us, everyone, every day."

"Tall order, isn't it?" she asked dubiously.

"It sure is. And that's my job. I have to create the kind of environment where the line hierarchy supports kaizen. This is why the boards are important. We can all meet in front of the board—from the CEO to the forklift operator—and we can challenge, listen, teach, and support. If we do it right we can figure out operations together, which translates into kaizen and step-by-step learning-by-doing. So we can all *learn together*.

"It's going well at the shipping dock, but believe me, it's not as good across the factory," he admitted ruefully. "But let's get back to

35

defining success. If you look at this board, you'll see that we've defined a production target for each hour of the shift.

HOUR	TARGET	ACTUAL	COMMENTS
1	68	56	
2	68	67	
3	68	65	
4	68	59	
5	68		
6	68		
7	68		
8	68		

Jane looked at the large whiteboard posted in the production cell across the alley. Then she watched the work. Five operators were assembling black plastic parts by passing them through tall square machines. In an oddly choreographed dance, they'd place components in the machine, then place the part, and then step back to let the machine operate, moving on to the next equipment, and so on. Each operator handled two or three machines in a continuous roundabout circle. She was depressed just looking at it. Imagine doing this for a living, day in, day out!

One of the operators saw them and nodded toward Ward, who crossed the alley and went to shake hands with a quick word for each. He looked right and left, and motioned her to come across.

"Stand in their shoes, look through their eyes," he said. "That's the secret to go and see. With this simple production board, we're leading. We're showing the team where we want to go, at a practical level, on an hourly basis, in terms of good parts to achieve per hour. They can see the goal at all times. And it is a common goal, since we all work at solving problems together in order to reach it. But this is only half the story. Look."

She stood there awkwardly watching while the team continued to work, some of them occasionally glancing over at them. What was she supposed to see?

"Technically, I have no clue, but this is interesting," she finally said pointing back toward the whiteboard. The comments column is not filled in."

"Well done," concurred Ward. "What does that tell you?"

"That the operators are not filling it in?"

"Not quite. Stand in their shoes, look through their eyes."

"Um. That they don't understand what it's there for?"

"Oh, they understand perfectly. What they don't see is *why*—the benefit to them. There are no comments because no one is interested in reading comments. If someone was looking at the board, operators would feel their opinions count, and they'd have something to say. We're not showing them respect, we're not showing interest in understanding the issues the team faces during the shift.

"We still have far to go here," he added with a slight wince. He pointed to the board. "The target column shows you how many parts we need to produce per hour. Here, it's 68—just over a part a minute. That's what we need to achieve to keep up with our customers' demand."

"But why break it down hour by hour?" Jane wondered aloud. "Wouldn't it make more sense to follow a cumulative chart to see if they're achieving the shift's production?"

"That's what they had before," nodded Ward. "And I asked them to change it. It's a matter of respect."

She suppressed a quick smile. Somehow, she'd known he'd say something like that.

"Building parts might look trivial to you," frowned Ward. "But it's important to these people. They come to work to *make good parts*. It might not be your thing, you prefer running a company that produces code. But you should respect their choice of occupation and not deny them the satisfaction of a job well done. It's exactly the same satisfaction whether we're discussing automotive parts, or bytes, or insurance claims."

"How's that?" she asked, ignoring his attitude.

"JOB = WORK + KAIZEN applies here just as much as everywhere else … although as I've pointed out, I've failed to get through to the plant manager so far. These people have the same right to succeed at their work today and in the future. That's the purpose of this target column," Ward said, walking to the chart and putting his finger on it. "*This* defines what we all agree by success."

"You set their objectives, is that it?" she asked, curious now.

"Yes, but there's a logic to it. We agree on the number of parts we should achieve per hour without any variability, at a natural work pace—no hurrying the job. The team and the supervisor measure the time it takes to make a part without mishaps. In practice we take the average of five cycles."

"You mean you don't allow for setbacks? How realistic is that?"

"That's the point. Our target is a *target*: the way we should work if nothing abnormal happens. It's not unrealistic because we've hit it at least five times in a row, so we can make it."

"Five times, fine, but sustaining that for an entire hour, or for a full shift?"

"Precisely. Look, the actual number produced is well under the hourly target."

"Are they not working fast enough?"

"It's got nothing to do with them!" exclaimed Ward. "Or at least not much. It's got to do with the working environment we managers offer them."

Delaney took a snapshot of the board, feeling she was completely missing some obscure point. She might have continued to ponder this mystery but Ward leaned in to share his thoughts.

"Look, I don't want to ask the operators right now, but I really need to have a chat about this with the plant manager and the area's supervisor. If you look at how these folks work, they're pretty steady and regular in their cycles. The reasons they miss the target are typically machine problems, missing components, quality issues, and so on. We, the system, are letting them down."

"It's about *you* again, is that it?" she frowned. Suddenly, it was not so funny any more as she thought how this just might apply back at Southcape.

"It's about us and them. It's about the relationship between management and employees. Just like with shipping. I can't personally control every single cell, and neither can the plant manager or the supervisor. Operators have to be autonomous and take responsibility for their own production. That's not merely permitted—it's expected.

"But if that's the case, then we've got to create an environment where they can step up and perform—where their ideas and opinions are respected. And where they can improve things step-by-step, by discussing issues they can't control with those who can. This is why the 'comments' column is about respect—every one on this team needs to know that what they think matters."

Ward suddenly became excited and pointed Delaney's attention across the floor.

"Look, did you see that? Something is wrong with the machine over there, and the operator has to stop what she's doing and … watch, she has to scramble past this other equipment and hit the reset controls. There. If this happens twice an hour that's one part lost.

"This is precisely the kind of item we want the operators to raise, and supervisors to work with their teams to resolve. As you can see, we've got ways to go before this sort of problem is written up on the board, but in some cells we're getting there. Come on, let's move on and let them get on with their work."

"Are you saying that you're trying to manage at that level of detail?" Delaney asked as they walked past the rest of the production area, her clunky toe-guards rasping on the concrete.

"What do you mean—detail?"

"What we saw. A few seconds within the hour?"

"Sure," grinned Ward. "The hour of production is the operator's world. It's about us getting into that world, not the other way around. Look, everyone wants to do a good job and we all want to get our problems fixed. The key is to respect that.

"Most managers struggle to teach operators their management problems: profitability, share price, and so on. Why would the guys in the shop care? Top brass prattles on about KPI. The guys on the floor call these numbers 'VIP-Is'—they are created for and shared by people high above their pay grade. These issues have nothing to do with their daily concerns and they're certainly not paid for it. Let the fat cats drawing the big paychecks worry about their strategy problems. And, if experience has taught operators anything, it's that any new management initiative is likely to end up as added pressure on them. So why even bother?"

Once again Ward had slowed his pace to a stop, almost inversely to the degree he was getting worked up. Delaney was intrigued. She couldn't help thinking back to all the times she got so frustrated at trying to explain to her staff what was good for the company only to meet flat, uninterested 'whatever' stares. She had always thought that it was because she was working with computer geeks and nerds. But maybe Ward was on to something.

"Respect as we practice it here—or try to," he corrected himself with a hesitation, "is about getting management to be interested in the operator's world: the team, the cell, the hour, even the second. Our collective success is built on every cell's success, every hour. So we have to get to that level of detail. We see this as work, where it counts, at the value-adding level. These guys are paying my wages with the work they do—and paying your fees as well—so I'd better take good care of them, don't you think?"

She nodded, thinking.

"Ah, I do get carried away," he sighed. "Come on, let's find a cup of coffee."

"No, no, wait. You're right, I just hadn't thought about it this way. Give me a second to think this through, okay? It makes perfect sense. You're saying that value is being created here, not in management meetings. Right. As a matter of fact, that's what the founder of our company believed, as well. He left all the management stuff to me because all he was interested in was the code. Bother!"

Ward started to say something, stopped, and then started again choosing his words carefully. "Now, just a second. I'm not saying that we don't need management, in fact just the opposite. What I'm saying is that we need the *right kind of management*. That's simple on the face of it, but hard to embrace, and a brutal challenge—at least for me it was—in terms of actual practice. Our job as managers is to create conditions where people can be successful at their job. And, what that comes down to is working together to solve the problems we face."

"It's obvious when you say it, but—"

"It's difficult to do. That's why it's a practice, not a theory. As I said, the practice here is to understand what customers value. What are their preferences? What puts a smile on their faces? What makes them contented, and what annoys them. We do this in order to define exactly what we mean when we talk about success.

"At the shipping dock, we determined that success was about getting every truck right and on time because automotive customers have a clear preference for getting exactly the right parts at the right time. In the production cell, success is about building the target amount of good parts every hour—and safely. None of this scrambling over equipment like we saw in that cell."

"Okay, I think I get it," she replied. "For each activity, you try to visualize success in an obvious way, like a scoreboard, so that everyone can agree on what success is. Then you want your management to work with their workers to overcome the barriers to that success. Is that what you mean by lead by respect?"

"There's more to, ahem, *lead with respect* than that," he smiled. "But it's certainly the starting point of leading from the front: being at

41

the workplace, visualizing success, and asking value-creating workers' opinions on what hinders us. This is why we call them 'production analysis boards.' We want to involve operators and their supervisors in joint analysis of what really happens in the cell, missed part by missed part. In some cases it works out fine, as you've seen in shipping where Tim worked with his guys to solve problems one-by-one. And in others, as you've seen here with the empty comments section, it doesn't. Which means essentially, I've got more training to do.

"This practice is not specific to production—we're doing this in some shape or form in every function of the company, from sales to design to PR. Everywhere. The core idea is that every person should own a clear target, a plan of how they intend to achieve it, and be able to spell out the problems they encounter on the way. I can't emphasize it enough. We're trying to systematically develop:

1. *Will power*: the commitment to reach the target even though obstacles are being thrown in the way of our original plan.
2. *Way power*: the capability to understand these problems and imagine alternative routes to achieving the target by solving problems one-by-one.

"These whiteboards might look silly to an outsider, but they are at the very heart of *lead with respect*. This is what we *do*."

"Let me see if I get this straight," Delaney said. "This is why you work with whiteboards. I was wondering about it. I mean, computers are easier and give you much better traceability. But you don't care about that, right? You want operators to physically write their target and their actual performance every hour, and then give their analysis of the gap so that they feel responsible for their results. Is that it?"

"Correct. We don't care about traceability because it all has to happen in the hour. If it's gone, it's gone. In fact, our ideal is reaction within the minute, but we're far from having the kind of managerial structure that would allow that here. We're getting there in my original plant, but it's taken years."

"You don't want management to solve the problems?"

"That's right. I want managers to work with operators to *deeply understand* the problems—which, by the way, starts by figuring out which problems are the ones they should be tackling in the first place! And I want managers to get suggestions from team members on how to solve the issues. Sure, I want to see production running smoothly. But more important, I want to see every person work to their full ability and contribute to the operation and improvement of their workplace. Yes."

"Wow."

"Oh, don't worry," he smiled sourly. "We've got a long, long way to go. As my CEO says, the largest room is the room for improvement."

"Some CEO you've got. He likes his clichés, apparently."

"We can agree there," chuckled Ward, as he guided her out of the production area toward the plant's offices.

––––––––––

They found a coffee machine and she sipped some tea while Ward stepped away to answer his phone. She wondered how her team was doing in the meeting. She glanced at her watch and was surprised to see they had now spent an hour on the shop floor. Her head was buzzing from the visit, too many new ideas too quickly. And every new concept made her feel more inadequate as a CEO. She had accepted the possibility that she was the problem just to make Ward feel good, but now she found she was seriously considering the thought. And it was not a nice feeling.

Inadequacy would not do, she chided herself. She had learned a few things about being a woman in a professional environment. One of which was that even the most uselessly incompetent male is often convinced he's doing a crackerjack job, whereas nice girls always wonder whether they're up to the challenge. If she'd learned one thing from her own career, it was that believing in herself was essential to driving others forward. So shut up with the doubts and get on with the job at hand: learn!

―――――――

"Thanks for taking the time to show me all of this, Andy," Jane said when he returned. "It's fascinating. Really."

"Well, thank you, too—really. It's always helpful for me to talk through this ... or try to. I've got eight plants and three engineering centers to run these days and my main stumbling block is finding a way to communicate this stuff so that people catch on. As you've seen on the shop floor out there, I've got miles to go. There's only so many times you can browbeat the same people, so saying it to someone new is good practice."

"Well, glad to be of help. There's something else you said that I'm still chewing on," she said. "This idea of defining success as a practice. I think I understand you, this is not something you just roll out. What you did in shipping is not the same as what you did in production. I mean, the spirit is the same, but not the actual boards and so on, they're all different. The way I should do it at my company should also be different—yet follow the same principles. By doing it over and over, you get better at it, right?"

"I would hope so, yes. That's the general idea. I used to think that because I had finally got the hang of it in one environment I could make it work in the next, but I found that's not the case. For instance, in the French plant where I started all of this, I'm trying to get the plant manager to work better with his maintenance team, and yet again, we stumble. We have to rethink completely how we define success with the maintenance guys. It's a relationship thing, never a given."

"I can see that. Definitely food for thought. One last question, if I may?" she asked.

"Please?"

"If I start from the premise that I am the problem ..." she smiled. "How do I define success for myself?"

"That's way above my pay grade," laughed Ward. "I'm not a CEO. Just a working stiff."

"Oh, come on, I'm serious. I've seen how you define success in various areas—"

"I would say, align success to value and commit to kaizen."

"Okay, align to value and commit to small step improvements. Got that. But what about my level?"

"I'm being serious. I'm not sure I can really help you there. But let me think." Ward stared into space to gather his thoughts. He finally answered her question with a question. "How would you define success?"

"I was just asking that myself!" she replied. "I would have said profitability, but I heard what you said about driving by looking at the rearview mirror. I can I agree with that. How about performance then, but of what?"

"If you forced me to answer," he said slowly, thinking it through, "I would say that on the financial side, it's pretty straightforward:
- Sales
- Cash
- Profit
- Capital Expenditure

"The question is what do we need to succeed at in order to improve the numbers. Phil clearly expects us to focus on a few core activities that he constantly reviews with us.

"First, *learn to see your problems*. This is true leadership from the ground up. You'd be surprised how hard people fight to believe the current situation is as it should be, not as it really is, and how often they shoot the messenger.

"Our 'problems first' attitude is the keystone of everything we do. Learning to distinguish a normal situation from abnormal one. And teaching everyone to see both the business problems and peoples' own problems. Understanding does not necessarily mean agreeing, but we need to understand the problems together if we want to ever have a hope of going forward.

"Second, *follow your customers*. Our customers are in a hyper-competitive environment and keep doing weird things—not all of them good. It's hard for us to keep pace with them and to know what actually satisfies them, as opposed to all the unreasonable demands they make on a daily basis. We try to figure out what they really value by constantly testing our ideas of what they want, what stable preferences they show consistently. We always feel we know better, but we have to admit that we don't. We need to constantly rethink where our customers are, where they're trying to go, and how we can support them. It's about solving their problems now, rather than trying to anticipate the problems they'll face in the future. I can think of a number of cases where this has led to genuine innovations, new markets and, in the end, sales.

"Third, *accelerate your flows*. That's very clear. Every time we've reduced customer lead-time and internal production lead-time, while maintaining our variety, we've gained market share. Fast is better than slow whichever way you look at it. In the factory it's about flexibility. In engineering it's about avoiding mistakes and rework, and coming up faster with an answer that works for everybody, from customer usage to manufacturing and supply chain.

"Yes, I'd say that accelerating flow is definitely a key to success, both because of the discipline of learning it imposes and the fact that inventory reduction generates cash improvements.

"Fourth, *develop your people*. What happens when you accelerate your flows is that you also accelerate the pace at which problems crop up and need to be dealt with. Autonomy in problem solving soon becomes essential just to cope. This means that people must be able to spot the right problem and solve it the right way without needing direct supervision.

"I've found out over time, that people start developing their personal vision of where they want to take their department. If we can agree on the general direction, this is the best guarantee for future success—sort of what you saw with Tim in outbound logistics. He's coming up with ideas I'd never have thought of in a thousand years, and I'm pushing the plant manager to centralize all the plant's logistics under him. The plant manager is resistant because he feels that Tim hasn't got the right schooling, but I couldn't care less. Success breeds success.

"Fifth, *be very good at a few things*. Phil keeps badgering me about this. He thinks I try too hard to make everything work and miss the forest for the trees. As the job keeps getting larger, we can't try to control everything. We need to focus on the few things that make us successful and not to worry about the rest. It'll sort itself out.

"Some fires can burn without having lasting impact, and people can make ad hoc decisions without requiring tight controls. It's back to the practice thing. There are a number of practices we work on continuously because we believe they make us better, and everything else will take care of itself. In terms of the financials, Phil feels this is the key to making smart investments, by distinguishing what matters from the rest and focusing on minimal technical solutions, which means looking for the simplest way to engineer an operation, as opposed to over-process or over-automate.

"Finally, *develop long-term partnerships*. Complexity keeps increasing and the competitive world is more turbulent than ever. Bad working relationships create untold waste in terms of energy, effort, and cash. We've been measuring the costs related to transferring production from one supplier to another because of quality, delivery, or costs problems, and the figures are astounding.

"And since we're focusing on being very good at a few things, we need to rely on others for the rest—hence our partnerships are essential," Andy said. "There are three dimensions which don't appear on our books but really make up the value of the company: our reputation with our customers, the competences of our people, and the mutual trust in our network of suppliers and partners."

"Something like this?" Jane asked, passing him her tablet on which she had quickly sketched his thoughts.

```
┌─────────────────────────────────────────────┐
│  ┌───────────────────────────────────────┐   │
│  │  Go and see and face your problems    │   │
│  └───────────────────────────────────────┘   │
│  ┌───────────────────────────────────────┐   │
│  │  SALES    Follow your customers        │   │
│  │  CASH     Accelerate your flows        │   │
│  │  PROFIT   Develop your people          │   │
│  │  CAP EX   Be very good at a few        │   │
│  │           things                       │   │
│  └───────────────────────────────────────┘   │
│  ┌───────────────────────────────────────┐   │
│  │  Develop long-term partnerships        │   │
│  └───────────────────────────────────────┘   │
└─────────────────────────────────────────────┘
```

"Hey, that's pretty good!" he exclaimed. "Yes, that's pretty much it."

"Wow again," said Delaney, rolling the pad's stylus between her fingers as she looked thoughtfully at her sketch. "Thank you for your answer. Since our first meeting I've been asking myself what I'm doing differently as a CEO from our founder who grew the company, and I'm starting to see what it might be. Because David let me do all the administrative work, I felt that if I met all the formal requirements the company would do well. It's always been a strength of mine, and I think that I came to believe that it was all that I needed to do to lead the company.

"Talking to you now, I fear I've lost sight of the ball. As you might say, I'm not scoring goals anymore. I'm worrying about the sponsors on the players' shirts. David always had a nose for where customers were going and what technologies to invest in. He was also very, very good at a few things. Come to think of it, he also spent a lot of time developing people. And I don't believe we've ever looked into accelerating flows. That's the stuff you lean guys are supposed to be good at, isn't it?"

"Good at? I doubt it," he chuckled. "We've been working hard at lean for years certainly, and accelerating flows is part of the story, but not how Phil would define it. He's got an equation for everything, and he describes lean as:

$$\text{LEAN} = \text{RESPECT} + \text{KAIZEN}$$

"A big part of getting the hang of lean involves recognizing where and how the pieces of the lean system fit together. We talk about accelerating flows, sure. But most newcomers to lean assume that we're talking about speeding up our work or improving our processes or boosting throughput.

"Here's the key: accelerating flows is no more than a technique to get problems to emerge. Think about it: the faster work flows through your processes, the faster problems come up. Also, we've found that accelerating flows tends to steer our attention toward the high-impact issues we might be tempted to ignore otherwise—kind of like having a compass for improvement. With hindsight, we can also see that accelerating flows radically changes what kind of investments we make, as we seek smaller, more flexible assets. In any case the real challenge is getting people to solve problems as they come up, which is what respect and kaizen are really about.

"Look, it all sounds very theoretical and blue-sky thinking, but we have found that if you reduce your customer complaints and cut your customer lead-time every year the business grows. And by accelerating flows and better using your assets, the business grows profitably.

"Oh, heck, look at the time," Andy cried as his phone buzzed. "I'm supposed to already be in another meeting, so I'm going to dash. I hope this visit has been useful. We can talk more on the phone in the next few days."

49

"Yes, thank you. Definitely," Jane said. "Now I'd better go see what shape my team is in—if your guys haven't beaten them into a pulp by now!"

Andy was through the door, asking someone to escort her back to the meeting room, and gone with a cheery wave.

She finished jotting down further notes about his six key points on her tablet. The plant's various whiteboards made her wonder where she could start using them at Southcape. "Wrong thinking," she chided herself. "Don't start copying what you don't understand. Start at the beginning. How do we define success?"

––––––––––

The weather was horrendous on the long drive back, with high winds and heavy rains, and the traffic was bad, but still she enjoyed driving, she always did. She had always loved speed and one of the perks of success was being able to afford a sleek, powerful car.

She knew about her reputation for driving like a maniac, but didn't care. Powerful German cars were her one real indulgence, and she had to admit to herself how much she enjoyed visiting the factory where engine parts were produced. She enjoyed meeting the people who actually conceived parts of the machine and then made them happen. She made a mental note to visit an automotive assembly factory one day.

Simon slouched on the passenger seat, saying little. Chris, on the other hand, was energized by the meeting. He spent most of the drive leaning forward between the headrests trying to engage them with all the brilliant things they could do with Nexplas.

Apparently the working session that took place while she and Ward toured the plant had ended up being productive. Her two guys had met with Nina Miah, the procurement manager, a procurement specialist named Stewart, and a couple of Nexplas IT guys whose names she didn't catch. They were impressed with the patches they had brought to fix Peter's code, and they demonstrated how they used the software and what they wanted to do with it.

"It's quite clever, really," Chris gushed. "Their problem is simple— and difficult. You see, they try to send their local suppliers an exact order of how many parts they want to pick up every day. Typically, this is done by their existing MRP on a stock-level replenishment basis. But that creates large fluctuations of demand on the supplier, so they're trying to do it another way. The first thing Peter made for them was a module that helped them break down their bill of materials by supplier. Now, you'd think this would be easy, but the data structure of their existing ERP is so lousy it turned out to be quite problematic. How they can operate with this thing, I don't know."

"I don't, either," confirmed Simon. "How did it go with the new boss? It sounds like this Ward guy is a real hard ass. They had planned to upgrade their whole IT system, but the first thing he did when he took over the company was to block all investments. Just like that."

"They planned to upgrade?" asked Jane, surprised.

"Sure? Didn't Rob tell you? That's how Peter ended up talking to them. When the plant canceled the upgrade after Nexplas bought them, he weaseled his way back in by promising he could fix things with their existing system. I think he shot us in the foot, because now there is no more question of upgrading."

Delaney knew she'd gotten involved late in the project, but she kicked herself for not having picked up more of the background. Certainly she had many other fires burning, but you'd have thought that she'd notice that one. She made a mental note to have it out with Rob next time she cornered him.

"In any case," Chris continued, "what they do now is produce an 11-week rolling forecast for each of their bought-out parts and send it to all suppliers to give them an idea of future numbers. If I understand this correctly, the Nexplas guys first asked them to do it by hand on a spreadsheet, so Peter really saved them when he automated that. His forecast summarizes parts requirements by production week. The quantities are divided by lot size to determine the number of lots to order for each part number. This means bringing up another database where they have a lot size negotiated with every supplier.

"Now currently, the orders they send to suppliers are based on this, but they'd like to go one further and factor in operating conditions at the factory to avoid over-ordering parts when they make changes or have difficulties."

"This means tracking variance to plan and including it in the ordering calculation?" Jane asked.

"Probably yes, though, frankly, in the current state of things, I have no idea how to make it work."

"I still think we should go to bat with a proposal to put in a whole new system designed to their requirements," Simon insisted.

"They won't go for it!" replied Chris adamantly. "Haven't you listened? They've got a budget to make minor improvements. They've got *no* budget for investments in new systems."

"Well, we need to persuade them! If we let them go on like this, we're at fault, as well," Simon blared. "Imagine we built patch after patch like this, it's going to be even more difficult to get back into a clean situation later down the line. Systems upgrade is what we do! Come on!"

Jane had been thinking about this, too. When she'd started with David, all the fun had been in exactly the kind of project Chris was getting excited about. They exploited the flexibility of PCs to come up with small, smart systems that helped their clients solve localized problems. As time went by and as their customers became more IT literate, they evolved into larger and larger projects, even supporting a couple of large in-house applications that the third director, Mike Wembley, was now managing.

In that sense, Simon was right: system upgrades had become what they did. They knew how to scope and staff larger projects, but now she wondered whether they had lost some flexibility along the way. The downside of large projects was that price competition had become crazy and margins were badly squeezed. She had checked Peter's billing with Nexplas. Overall turnover was small, but profit was somewhat higher that what she was accustomed to seeing with large projects.

"I think Chris is right," she said. "Their VP mostly discussed their 'kaizen,' which I understand is about breaking down large changes into small, continuous-improvement steps. They *prefer* small steps."

"Yep, that's what they asked for," exclaimed Chris excitedly. "They kept saying step-by-step improvement."

"It might work for manufacturing," muttered Simon, "but it makes no sense in what we do. If your platform is crap, there's no point in tinkering with it!"

"Oh, I don't know," said Chris. "Look at what they manage to do with Peter's hack job. They're grumbling about how it still requires a lot of manual input, but they're doing what they want to do, right?"

"We're not helping them, I'm telling you. We're just letting them continue to walk down a blind alley. There's nothing in it for either them or us."

"That, I believe, is the real question," Jane stepped in. "What's in it for us? Do we want to follow our customer? They're quite clear in what they value. They're actually beating us over the head with it. They want constant small changes in order to learn to do what they're trying to do. They've repeatedly said no to large investment. Their VP has gone out of his way to lecture me on small-step improvement. This is what they value. The question is, do we want to sell it to them?"

"I'm game," jumped in Chris immediately.

"Sure, I'm in," agreed Simon. "After all, they are a strategic client —and a revenue stream is a revenue stream. But we're going to regret this, I can tell."

———

How does one define success? Jane asked herself for the thousandth time as she looked up from her laptop.

She had decided to spend a rare Saturday with the girls rather than the office, but couldn't resist the siren call of work and had set up shop at the breakfast table.

The week had shaken her up, for sure. She had been investigating the auto-testing that Peter had raved about before leaving the company. The idea was quite simple. Rather than have all the final testing done after the code was built, developers were supposed to check their code as they wrote it with automated tests. She had heard about this on and off, but no one had really picked it up at Southcape.

When she asked Chris about it he steered her to Terry Boyle, one of their younger recruits and, she discovered, an 'agile' computing fanatic. He was also a member of what she called the T-shirt brigade. They couldn't articulate a full sentence to save their lives, but they expressed themselves at work by wearing statement T-shirts.

She had long dismissed the agile rage as a fad, but after the plant visit she'd looked up the agile manifesto again. The 'intent to value individuals and interactions over processes and tools, working software over comprehensive documentation, customer collaboration over contract negotiation, and responding to change over following a plan' sounded pretty close to what Ward had been saying. So maybe, just maybe, all the things he had said could be relevant to software development. And maybe she would have to change her mind about how she viewed agile development methods.

It grated her, but she had to acknowledge the fact that under her leadership, Southcape had come to value processes and tools over people, procedure over working code, contract negotiations over collaboration, and roadmaps over change. She wistfully remembered when she had been one of the young turks, joining David's startup to prove to all the mainframe IT guys what could be done with PCs. Now it seemed she was the one fending off new thinking, such as

Boyle's agile development or Mike Wembley's cloud obsession. 'Face your problems,' she'd been told. Oh blast it!

When she had gone looking for Boyle, she found him deeply engrossed in his code. The back of his black T-shirt read: *Those who think they know everything annoy those of us who actually do.* It had made her laugh. Now she had some of his code on her laptop and was trying to make sense of it. Bother, if it didn't make her feel a generation behind.

When had she last actually written code? She had to be honest with herself and admit that she'd gotten to where she was without ever really asking that question.

Born in the early sixties, she'd moved straight from nun's school to a hippie commune. She lived with two mates rehabilitating derelict barges on the Thames and looking for mischief. Eventually she wanted more and found a job as a bank clerk. She gravitated toward the computer department, where she was a natural, back in the days when—oh, she didn't even want to remember. She got married in her early thirties, then the girls were born, and a few years later her scumbag husband scuttled off leaving her with a four-year-old and a baby—just as she was leaving the bank to join David's crazy venture.

She never had the time to look back since. Success? What success? She had two gorgeous daughters, her own house, a Batmobile, and enough money in the bank to never worry about rainy days. She was the CEO of her own company. Well, the bank's company, really. How many of her peers could say that?

But she was failing! She knew it in her bones.

She was not leading Southcape, she was being led by it. Running as fast as she could just to stay in place. She had been annoyed by Ward's casual arrogance, his hero worship of his boss, his unthinking assurance that he had something to teach her, just as he had something to teach his direct reports. He seemed to think that his job was to teach people rather than run things.

But she recognized that he had a clear idea of what he was doing and where he wanted to go—and the man was a good 10 years younger than she was! And it bothered her more than she could say that what he said reminded her of David so often. Define success. Commit to kaizen. Be very good at a few things …

———————

Well, she told herself wryly as she snapped her laptop shut, there's one thing I'm very good at.

"Ladies," she announced, "it's stopped raining, and I think it's time we hit the high street."

Both girls looked up with the exact same look of pleasant surprise.

"Mom?" asked her eldest in mock worry. "You okay?"

"Never better, my sweet," she said with a smile. "Come on, let's move, I'm springing today."

Chapter Three

MANAGING BY
PROBLEM SOLVING

"It's not working!" Delaney exclaimed.

"Er ... what's not working?" Ward asked.

"All of it! None of it. I've tried to define success for every one of our projects. I've got them to post their projects plans on the walls. Every one complains, and if anything, the situation is even more chaotic."

"Well, I don't know exactly what things are like at your workplace, but I can tell you that whatever you are doing is working for us. Last time I checked with Nina, she was pleased with something your graphics expert did. She feels like we were making progress."

"Pleased with Sharon?"

"Yes ... I think. But tell me exactly what's not working?"

"Oh, I don't know," she sighed. "You've got a lot on your plate, I shouldn't bother you with this."

"It's all right, go ahead."

"Well," she said, taking a deep breath. "Here's the thing. I've been thinking about what you said about success and customer complaints and lead-time, yes?"

"Sure, and?"

"In our case, I've focused on rework, re-releases, and customer lead-time, from when we get the go ahead for the project to actual delivery. I've asked every project manager to highlight rework, which opened another can of worms, as many can't make the difference between right-first-time and rework. To them rework is normal."

"Okay. Any idea why?"

"I think so. My hunch is that the project scope often moves in the course of the project itself. Neither the clients nor us are very specific about the scope upfront, so as we show them stuff and as their internal situation evolves, so does the project scope. My project managers lose any distinction between rework caused by early misunderstanding, coding mistakes, or moving targets. Quite the headache!"

"Great. Sounds like you're making progress in understanding your problems. And?"

"It's a mess," Jane groaned. "I've been gathering the data from the past five years and discovered that our re-release rate has been steadily increasing ... and so has our lead-time."

"And your profitability?" Andy quizzed.

"Ah ..." she hesitated, not sure about how far she was willing to confide in a client. "Reduced," she finally owned up.

"It doesn't show much because we've been taking in larger projects for the past three or so years. Turnover has increased and the firm's profit remained okay. But profitability as a percentage of sales has steadily eroded. And this year looks bad. We've lost some major bids. As I said, it's a mess."

"Actually, I'm hearing good news," Andy replied encouragingly.

"How can any of that be good?"

"Not pleasant, but good. Look, you're definitely making progress."

"I am? It doesn't feel like it!"

"*Problems first*," Ward replied, "is the basic attitude that underlies our success. I realize this sounds paradoxical, but every other aspect of learning to *lead with respect* is tied to our ability to face our problems —and when we do, not to ask who, but why?

"And I believe that this is what I'm hearing. You're facing your problems. Be careful now. My experience is that your first hunch is rarely wrong as such, but almost never right. Changes in problem scope sounds likely. But I suspect that assumes it's more the fault of the clients causing the lead-time and profitability slippage. You need to investigate until you've figured out exactly what is happening and why. As I said, it probably doesn't feel like it, but this is a break-through moment. Face your challenges with courage and creativity and you'll be fine."

"I'll have to take your word for it," she answered, impatient with his platitudes, "because right now, I'm stumped."

"Look, I can't talk more right now, but if you like, I'll be visiting the Swindon site next week. Since your offices are close to Heathrow, I can stop by on the drive back to the airport and take a look at what you're doing."

"That would be great, but I don't want to put you out—"

"No worries, I'm curious, as well. My assistant will let you know my travel plans. Gotta run. Bye!"

"Problems first!" Jane sighed as she tossed her mobile on her desk. "Problems everywhere, yes!" She was both relieved and worried that Ward would visit. She conceded to herself that it would be naïve to think that the situation would improve magically just by looking into things. Nonetheless, she had been taken aback by the extent of the mess she had uncovered.

In an attempt to visualize success, she had asked every project team to post their project plan on the wall, with a clear delivery date marked on paper. At first the teams outright ignored her, responding only when she gathered all the project leaders and told them to do it. No arguments! Then every day she was in the office she started spending a couple of minutes with each project leader, soliciting their views on how they saw things developing. This unleashed a barrage of problems of all kinds, most of which she did not have an answer to.

She had made a lot of suggestions at first, only to learn that the team had already thought about the most obvious ideas and were stumped by deeper problems. She eventually learned to just listen. This invariably left an awkward pause at the end of the visit when they all looked at her, waiting for a direction she did not know how to give, other than to say 'good job, carry on.'

She often felt like dropping the whole thing, yet when she thought about how much she was learning about the company's main projects she resolved to take her licks and keep going.

One of the biggest surprises was discovering how vague most project leaders were about both the project definition and the status of their current situation. They had weekly management meetings in which every project leader presented a progress report, and barring the usual customer issues, the general impression was that all was going more or less according to plan. But when she cornered them with their teams and looked into the details of the planning, she kept getting hums, haws, and gray areas. Milestones, in particular, seemed to be a relative concept, either changed by the clients themselves or blown by the team due to unexpected issues or scoping changes.

In the end, the sure thing was that testing time always got eaten up, which was one of the reasons the software went out of the door with so many unresolved bugs. That, she felt, was something she could do something about.

She also needed to talk to Sharon Miller, who was self-effacing to the point of fading into the walls. It was galling to hear from the client that she had done something good that no one knew about.

In the past week, her list of live issues had exploded exponentially. 'Problems first' was all good and well, but what about a few solutions for a change? It was time for support from a reliable source.

———

"Ah, I do love a wine that fights back," Mike Wembley said mischievously as he swirled the Chianti, raising his eyebrows. He was Southcape's Technology Director and celebrity geek. He'd evolved beyond a daily role, spending most of his time on the speaker circuit these days, a move that Delaney had resented at first, but learned to appreciate. She always had a good relationship with him, and his high profile brought them a steady flow of leads.

"Any thoughts about test-driven development?" Jane asked.

"Many, dear girl, many. It's mostly the practice of writing tests for code before writing the code itself. Can you be a little more specific?"

"These days we rarely release cleanly because of the number of bugs we miss at the testing phase. This means a lot of re-releases and cheesed-off customers. I've been wondering whether we could improve our quality level if we taught our developers to do their own testing."

"It's been tried on and off by the big guys, but rarely successfully."

"Do you know why?"

"Not sure. Probably one of them culture things. The concept is alluring, but the reality of getting every developer to buy into it and learn how to do it is another matter."

"Would you know how?" she asked, hopefully.

"Possibly," he answered cautiously, tipping the end of the bottle into both their glasses. "But …"

He stared at the glass for a few moments, lost in thought. He was a stout middle-aged man with a shock of unruly white hair. She wondered fondly how on earth he had so skillfully shifted his persona from the paunchy geek she had first met to the genius-dash-eccentric, darling of the media? She could forgive him everything but his penchant for wearing stripes with stripes, the pinstripes of his suit jarring with the colorful stripes of his shirt and tie badly enough to give one a headache.

"I'd need a free hand. This is not a small task, and it would mean that I'd have to get back into the company more than I have the past couple of years."

"Would you want to?"

"Why not? I'm almost done with my book tour and although I enjoy being your, ahem, chief technologist, sometimes one does spend too long away from the code, you know? Would probably do me good. But …"

"But what, Mike?" She loved him dearly and truly respected his technical brilliance, but he could be so exasperating!

"I have some ideas of where this will go and you're not going to like what you'll find."

"We used to be good, Mike. We used to be damn good."

"We were the best," he smiled.

"Can we be again? Or was it all David's magic touch?"

"Are you asking whether you can make us great, Jane?"

She stared at him, lost for words.

"You can, you know," he answered for her, tapping his nose conspiratorially. "You've finally started asking the right questions. I have a feeling that this company is going to get interesting again. Testing, boss?"

"Testing," she nodded, letting go of a breath she hadn't realized she'd been holding.

"I get to do it the way I want to?"

"Carte blanche."

"This," he suddenly laughed, "is going to be *fun*."

———

"You've got to *listen to people*," said Ward reviewing the large project plan posted on the wall. "They've got to *feel their opinions count*."

He didn't look good. He had a nasty cough and black circles under his eyes. He had showed up late and was already late to catch his flight. Southcape offices were located in an industrial park right by Terminal Four, but the traffic could be unpredictable.

"We discuss a lot," she replied defensively.

"But do you listen?" he asked again, softening the remark with a tired smile. "Look, I'm delighted to see project plans posted on the walls, that you're tracking what ... rework? Yes? Fine. Now you have to go back to the basics of *lead with respect*: stand in their shoes and look through their eyes. What is the impact on the teams?"

She took a deep breath and thought hard. Even after many conscious efforts to adopt this position, she still found it surprisingly difficult to look at the situation from her employees' perspective.

"Pressure," she finally said. "Added pressure."

Someone sniggered behind them, with a muttered "ha!" loud enough to be heard by all. Delaney glared at Terry Boyle, who had been typing on his laptop a few feet away with his back turned to them, headphones grafted to his ears.

"Thank you, Terry," she said coldly. "If you want to join the conversation, please feel free."

He turned around with an easy smile, a small round dark bloke with a laidback manner—very laid back.

"You know what I mean," he said. "You pepper us with questions about why we're late on this or that. We know we're late. And your questions don't actually help us. In fact they just stress out the project leader more."

"It's an easy mistake to make," coughed Ward. "I did the same thing myself when I turned around my first plant. I got so intent on pushing everyone to reach their targets that they went on strike."

"Well, they were French, weren't they," said Delaney, trying to joke about it.

"Yes," Ward answered with a tight smile. "Just like my wife."

"Ah, um, touché? Let's get back to these boards, please. Now that we can see what the targets are, we can see that we're not meeting them. What do we do?"

"Let me start by asking, why you post the numbers on a board for everyone to see?" Ward let that sit for a moment and then answered his own question, "Teamwork. The point of go and see is to grasp the real place, real people, and real relationships. We don't want to pressure people to work harder. That won't get us very far. We want them to work smarter by working better together, so they don't waste each other's time with nonvalue-added stuff. We want to understand the waste caused by problems and misunderstandings so that we can solve them *together*." He looked at the board carefully, and added, "You're doing exactly the same thing you noticed in my plant. See?"

Delaney stared blankly. She had no idea what he was referring to.

"Do you recall that production analysis board you saw with the empty comments section?" he asked. "You spotted it yourself: not much analysis done there, remember?"

"Is that what we're doing?" she wondered aloud. "No space for comments?"

"Precisely. But more importantly, ask yourself why this section matters. We visualize these types of things so that we can see together, know together, and act together. Here we can see that we're behind target. However, the board does not show that we understand why or what we're doing about it."

"Isn't that the project manager's job?"

"Partly, yes. But let's keep thinking about lead with respect. It's her job to listen to every team member's opinion and make these opinions count."

"But what if their opinion is wrong?"

"Fair enough. Understanding doesn't mean agreeing. Find a way to convey neither 'yes' or 'no,' but simply that you've heard what they've said. No one is tied by anyone's opinion. That's the whole point. We want to visualize opinions precisely, so that we can discuss them as a team. What's more, since team members are the closest to the problem, what they have to say is *always* helpful. We need to listen to them."

"So we just put up a section for comments and that's that?" she asked dubiously.

"Here, use this," Ward said, walking over to a flipchart in the corner of the room. He divided the paperboard in six columns. "Every day, as the project leader reviews the plan, ask her to write down at least one full analysis with her team. The idea is to specify:

- The problem as we currently understand it, the more specific the better.

- The presumed cause—just ask why?
- What we intend to do about it.
- Who is impacted by this problem and should be brought into the conversation?
- The status—on track, delayed, or abandoned."

Date	Problem	Cause	Countermeasure	Who does it concern	Status

Delaney studied it with a bit of detachment. "It sounds very formal. How does it help?"

"Ah," replied Ward. "Let's assume that our performance problems are caused by problems that we encounter routinely but don't know how to solve easily. Agreed?"

"That—or we are trying to solve the wrong problems."

"Good. Now, respect for our team means that we don't leave them alone with a problem. This defines our management role: we're basically here to help operators work unhindered."

"Except that we don't know how to do that."

"Correct. We don't know how to do that. So we've got to learn— hence the paperboard."

"So ... you're introducing a new practice, here, yes? This 'problems first' bit. You're saying that by writing down our problems one by one we can then review how well we solve them ... and, I would imagine, learn to do so better over time?"

"That's exactly what I'm saying—and what's more, we do this as a team. Teamwork is a *skill*. It's essentially about learning to solve problems across boundaries: hierarchical boundaries as well as functional boundaries. Look, this is all very theoretical. Let's just try it.

"Hi there, young man," Ward said, turning toward Terry, who'd gone back to his screen. "You were saying the project was late, and that you all knew what the causes are. What did you have in mind?"

"My computer is slow, for starters," Terry answered with a smile that was anything but friendly.

Delaney hoped that Ward did not see her rolling her eyes.

"There you go," said Ward, without batting an eye. "Would you write this down for us, please? I'm just trying to demonstrate how this practice works."

"Sure," the young man said, getting up and writing carefully 'computer is slow' on the paperboard. Today's T-shirt said *7 out of 3 people are math illiterate.*

"Why do you think that is?" asked Ward.

"Software I'm running on it is too heavy for the memory."

"And why is that?"

"Can't get an upgrade," Terry shrugged, with a side-glance toward Delaney, who stood tight-lipped and arms crossed.

"And the countermeasure would be?"

"New computer?"

"Too easy," smiled Ward. "We first look for solutions without investment. Any other ideas?"

"I don't know. I guess I've been meaning to dump some of the other stuff on the machine and haven't got around to it yet."

"I thought we had scheduled dust-off sessions?" Jane interjected. "Aren't we supposed to get rid of unnecessary and unused programs regularly?"

The kid shrugged.

"Do you think that's the cause?" asked Ward.

"Sure, we carry so much stuff that some programs are bound to get in each other's way," Terry finally agreed grudgingly. "But there's never any time to do proper maintenance, and it's not so easy. Every time you touch something, you can affect something else. A new computer is still likely to be the most effective way of solving this, at the speed the tech evolves."

"Everybody is always complaining their computers are slow," exclaimed Jane, "including me."

"We're not dealing with everybody," Ward replied. "We're dealing with this problem, here and now. We're dealing with the way this computer slows the work and how the project leader deals with it.

"That's the first problem that comes to mind, but I'm sure that there are others. Don't you see? It's like the operators we saw on the cell you visited, who had to cope with restarting one of the machines all the time. They should not have to do that. It stops them from achieving their targets."

Ward just stood there as Delaney fumed. The silence became increasingly uncomfortable, as neither would add anything. After a few very long seconds, Terry chirped in his mock-helpful manner, "Right, I'd better be going back to work," and slouched back to his computer.

"My office?" she said coldly.

"Sure," answered Ward uneasily.

———

"What just happened?" asked Ward, as he sat down at the round table in her office, racked by another fit of coughing.

'Keep your germs to yourself, young man,' Delaney thought, walking around her desk. She fidgeted with the papers waiting for her signature, asked her assistant to bring them some tea, and gave Ward a chance to recover from his coughing before responding.

"I got slapped in the face, that's what!"

"Did you?"

"Or ... I'm the problem. That's what you think, isn't it?"

He looked at his hands, saying nothing, but the sides of his mouth curved slightly.

"Goodness, this is hard," she finally said.

"Learning always is," he said supportively. "You just stood in this guy's shoes and looked through his eyes. What he sees is a slow computer and pressure on deadlines."

"And callous managers who don't give a damn. I get it. As a boss what I see is people always carping and asking for newer, shinier, and pricier toys."

"That's part of it, but not the most important aspect. The question is: Why was this conversation so difficult?"

"What do you mean?"

"Well, it wasn't an easy chat, was it?"

"Bloody awkward."

"But why?"

"Because … because …," she thought hard. The process was more painful than she'd expected. "It's a bit self-fulfilling. They're hard simply because they're always hard. We just don't know how to have these conversations, we don't know how to address the problems of our employees. Is that it?"

"Spot on. And believe it or not, this paperboard helps enormously. It provides a method, a language, for having this kind of difficult conversation—and for grounding your talk in the work and not the people. Defining success in the categories of this board helps because it structures the conversation. You want people to be:
  - Specific about the problem
  - Insightful about the cause
  - Clever about the countermeasure
  - Open minded about who else is concerned
  - Rigorous about status checks

"Remember what I said about developing will power and way power? We want people to carry through the problem solving and not stop at the first setback. We want them to learn to explore alternatives and discover deeper causes. The board is a method to do so. It defines successful problem solving. In doing so, it helps you support your project managers in getting their teams to think the right way, and to eventually learn how to work with their teams to remove all the barriers that stand in the way of success. This is teamwork. Again, it's a practice."

"But how do you practice teamwork, team building, and such?"

"By problem solving. We build teams by getting them to solve their own problems together, and then teaching them how to get better at it. Another way of thinking about lead with respect is *managing by problem solving*."

"Like your guy in the shipping dock?"

"The same."

"But how do I do this?" Jane grumbled. "I spent weeks learning about the problems that my workers have. Then when I tried to solve them I felt like an idiot, because they had already considered a lot of my ideas. I can't solve all their problems. Not only that, but as you just saw: any conversation about problems usually just gets folks annoyed or suspicious."

"Yes," Ward replied. "I won't argue with that. However, the practice of managing by problem solving uses one simple word for this: *why?* You don't have to solve problems for people. You don't have to react. Just do what I do: Ask why?"

"Ask why? That's it?" Delaney asked doubtfully.

"Essentially, yes. Just ask why? At your level, you're not trying to solve every problem. You're aiming to build better relationships between your developers and their managers, so that they can solve their own problems. You ask them to clarify what they think the problem is, then to clarify their understanding of the cause you ask 'why?' And 'why?' again. And then you clarify the effectiveness of their countermeasure by asking them whether they've checked the status and what conclusion they draw from their action."

"You keep saying countermeasure. Don't you mean solution?"

"It's a lean tic," he admitted. "We don't believe in permanent solutions. No process is ever perfect, there's always room for kaizen; hence an immediate countermeasure, or deeper countermeasures to address root causes. Countermeasures are closer to remedies than solutions, if you see what I mean."

"I think so—not sure."

"Well, we keep in mind an ideal situation—or the standard—and then see a problem as a gap between what is currently going on and this ideal. A countermeasure is a remedy that would get us back to the ideal. It's very important to understand the power of defining a problem as simply a gap between what is and what should be. This assumes that the individual understands what should be—which is a big step. It assumes that two people talking are trying to understand this gap in a way that can be improved. When you see a problem like this, it enables you as a manager to stand side-by-side with your worker to break down the gap."

"Um. Okay. So I just ask why? And then not give them an answer, right? Just leave them hanging?"

"It's a practice! Asking 'why?' is a practice. Do it a few million times and see your understanding of asking 'why?' change. Sure folks will respond defensively at first, this is only human. And besides, they're used to managers shooting the messenger."

"As I did with Terry a minute ago."

"Yeah," he grinned. "In the eyes of staff, management is always about some rule or other they haven't applied correctly. Asking 'why?' is in fact about seeking the root cause of the problem collaboratively. You must practice consistently asking why—and not who? Most people get emotionally attached to the first response that comes to mind, which stops the problem-solving cycle as each stakeholder anchors on their first idea. If everyone acknowledges we're going to ask 'why?' several times, we can break through this instinctual barrier and actually share our thinking, which is the first step to real teamwork.

"Basically, you ask 'why?' repeatedly until the most obvious answers are swept off the table and people finally consider the real problem together. Yes, it does take practice. And it's usually awkward as hell. But it's important to wait it out. Silence doesn't necessarily mean sulking. It can also mean they're finally thinking with their heads rather than their mouths.

"Asking 'why?' sounds simple. But it really is another fundamental part of lead with respect." Ward counted on his fingers:

1. Put the customer first
2. Go and see
3. Show respect
4. Ask why?"

"It sounds awfully simple when you say it like this," Jane replied. "Is that what we did?"

"Well, yes, kinda. We went to where, ah, Terry is working and asked why the delivery to the customer was late. We showed respect by making an effort to stand in his shoes and look through his eyes, and to understand his point of view—and we asked 'why?' I'm not saying it's effortless, but that's the *practice*, yes."

"I'm sorry, it's hard to take it on faith. And no disrespect, but this is going to solve the company's woes?"

Ward rubbed his face tiredly and glanced down at his watch. He looked like death warmed over. She suddenly felt sorry for the poor guy.

"Listen, Andy," she said. "I don't want to kick you out, but if you stay here much longer you might find yourself with another problem at the airport!"

"I'll be off," he smiled, getting out the chair. "But before I go, though, could I have a quick word with the woman that does the graphics work on our project?"

"Sharon Miller? Sure!"

They found Sharon working at her desk.

"Hi Sharon," said Andy, in greeting. "How are you doing today?"

"Oh, hi, Mr. Ward! Very good, thank you," answered Sharon.

Jane noted with amusement that she was blushing. She was a pale woman, tall and angular, with deep green eyes. She was a hard worker, but easily flustered and painfully shy.

"Nina told me she was very happy with the graphic display you did for the supplier assessment."

"Oh, good!"

"Sharon's done a graph that plots all our suppliers by missed deliveries and bad parts," Andy explained to Jane. "We can click on outliers and the identity of the supplier comes up—with real-time data. This is exactly what we needed to get started on our supplier program, which is one of the things the CEO has tasked me with this year. So thank you, Sharon."

"Oh. You're welcome," she replied, with a nervous smile.

"By the way, would you have a talk with Nina about doing the same sort of thing for HR? I'd be interested to see a graph of our personnel by compensation and seniority."

"Certainly. I will. Yes."

"That'd be great. Good work, thank you," he said, shaking her hand and hurrying toward the lobby.

"Thank you," said Jane, as she asked one of the guys to drive him to the airport rather than order a cab—quicker that way.

"No problem."

"I mean it, thank you. I'm not having an easy time of it, as you probably can tell. But I'm ever more convinced that I need to learn this stuff. Thank you also for taking the time to talk to Sharon. She really appreciated it."

"Well, we need to let people know how they're getting on, don't we? Part of the job, right?"

"Um. Yes, I guess so."

"I've been thinking," Andy said, as the car pulled in front of them. "Why don't you schedule another visit at the plant? You need to see the area where we've got most of this working, particularly the visual management aspect. I realize that working with computers all day long this might not be as intuitive, but I think you'll find it interesting."

"Will do, certainly. With pleasure."

"Ask Ann to let you know next time I'm there. Bye now!"

"Have a safe trip!" she said, as he rushed out under the rain and dove into the waiting car.

Andy hunkered down in his seat as the plane lurched suddenly on its approach to Frankfurt. He really felt poorly and thought he should be going home to Claire and the kids, rather than to deal with more engineering headaches. But on the other hand, he feared he'd caught a bad bug, so better not pass it on to the baby.

Besides, it was an exciting time. They had won the contract for a new German top-of-the-line model, which he felt looked terrific and hopefully would sell like hot cakes. They won the bid by offering to replace what was traditionally a metal part with one of their plastic castings and every one had been very happy about the cost numbers— and from his side, the sell price. But now that the start of production was looming closer, the car engineers were getting jittery and there were a host of issues to resolve. He needed to be there often to hold his guys' hands and clear the way with management on both sides, so that they could concentrate on product issues.

He loved the job, but the traveling was getting to him, particularly in winter. He organized it so that he stayed at home on Fridays and Mondays, but had to travel the rest of the week, every week. The discipline of go and see took him to a different plant each day, which was kind of cool for certain, but could be exhausting.

And he was worried about the Swindon plant. The site had a troubled recent history, having changed hands twice rapidly before being acquired by Nexplas. Jenkinson had purchased the plant mostly because it made parts for two Japanese U.K. plants, and had done a song and dance about quality to get those contracts renewed.

Operations had been badly mauled by two waves of cost cutting and the plant manager Len Barton was a survivor of several management cutbacks. He got things done, no question about it, and knew how to keep his nose clean. But he got results by running equipment and people into the ground and then begging for replacements. Ward simply didn't know how to get him to understand that the gap between 95% efficiency and 99% wouldn't be closed by more challenging, but by greater listening, teaching, and support.

If he was honest about it, part of the difficulty was that he didn't like Barton personally. The man was a bully, running the site through a network of cronies, using the production manager as his enforcer, and ruthlessly discouraging any independent thinking for fear of attracting upper-management attention.

Barton couldn't get it through his thick skull that there was no upper management beyond himself and Phil, and that what they sought was the kind of initiative and creative thinking displayed by supervisors like Tim in shipping, rather than the strongman attitudes embodied by the current production manager, who was a close buddy of Len's but totally impervious to anything other than reward your friends and punish your enemies. He realized that if he forced Barton to fire the production manager, he would be caught red handed in "do as I say, not as I do."

Since he wasn't about to lose Barton and his mate, he had to find a way to work with them. So far, he'd done it by spending time with the few supervisors who understood what he was trying to do in the hope that Barton would wake up to the change of management style expected of him.

He thought back to his plant tour with Jane and how she picked up that the production analysis boards were used to push for parts rather than discuss problems with the operators. Ironically, she'd reproduced exactly the same mistake with her project plans on the wall. Thankfully, she hadn't seen what he saw as they toured the plant. He felt like a right fraud, lecturing about lead with respect in that site.

Andy was jolted out of his momentary funk as the plane touched down rather roughly, and he started thinking gloomily about the long drive in the snow to the hotel. On the bright side, visiting Southcape had cheered him up. There were never any guarantees, but Jane was trying hard, which surprised him pleasantly. He hoped fervently that what she had started would pay off, because the truth was he had no clue about what they were showing him. He could only stick with what he knew: challenge people, listen to them, teach them to solve their own problems, support them in doing so, and somehow get them to work better with each other. One thing was for sure, he was discovering a new field and that was fun.

"I'm sorry, Jane, that just won't do!"

"Rob? Do come in," she said with heavy sarcasm as he had already stomped into her office. She wondered what the point of being the boss was if you were taken to task by everyone, from the most junior programmer to the sales director—not even counting clients.

"What's got you so upset then?"

"I'm not upset!" he replied, pacing back and forth in front of her desk. He'd been putting on a lot of weight lately, and losing some of his rakish good looks. The tan in winter didn't help either, making him look like an aging beau. He was back from his yearly winter vacation in Antigua, but it didn't seem to have mellowed him much this time around.

"You know what's wrong. The most senior European executive of one of our major clients is in house and I'm not even invited!"

"I sent you an email."

"An email? Are you kidding? Do you know how many emails I get a day?"

"Are you saying you don't read my emails?" she frowned.

"I'm saying nothing of the sort!" he retorted. "I'm saying that as Sales Director I'd like to be kept in the loop when our clients show up —and to know why! I don't understand what's happening with this Nexplas deal anyhow, now that you've pulled Simon out of there."

"I haven't pulled Simon out of anything," she replied calmly. "He had to wrap up the MRX project and was not happy with the way Nexplas was going. Chris has been doing a good job and is enjoying it. I fail to see what the problem is."

"There's no talking to you anymore. How do you expect Sales to sell if developers start working directly with clients? We've got a process and you know it. Sales define requirements, the project leader writes the specs, and the team develops and tests. That's the way we work."

"And this has worked so well for us, hasn't it?" she almost cried out, exasperated. "We've been doing so well, haven't we?"

"I keep landing bigger and bigger fish," he puffed.

"From which we're not making any more money."

"That's an operational matter, nothing to do with Sales."

They stared each other down. She had a sudden flash of how intense work relationships could be at times. And how the most attractive trait of a person becomes the most unbearable as time goes by. Rob was a great salesman. He could be full of charm and focus. But his narrow-mindedness and self-regard drove her crazy.

"Listen, I had a chat with Mike," she said, changing the subject. I was thinking about reinstating Wednesday night drinks at Giovanni's."

"You know I can't make it in the evening. I've got a much longer drive than any of you have."

'So much for teamwork,' she thought. "How about lunch then? On Wednesdays?" she offered.

"I'll put it in my diary and see if I can make it."

"I'd rather appreciate it if you would," she said coldly.

They glared at each other some more. He seemed to be about to say something, but then turned around and stormed out.

That went well, she thought to herself with a weary sigh, absently rubbing the polished wood of her desk. She couldn't remember their last real conversation about the state of the business.

Rob was another burning issue she'd been avoiding. Although she was the CEO, she, Mike, and Rob had equal shares in the partnership, the majority being held by the equity firm. It had seemed like a good idea at the time, since none of them had enough cash to buy David out. She smiled wryly, remembering the joke about the guy who ran out in the desert and sat on a cactus. When asked why he had done that, he replied that, at the time it had seemed like a good idea.

––––––––

"Welcome, I'm Len Barton, the site manager," said the man shaking her hand in the lobby. He could have been the thinner brother of the chap she'd seen in logistics the last time, with similar intense features, deep-set gray eyes, and short shorn scalp shining in the neon light. "Andy apologizes, but he couldn't make it. He's stuck in Germany," he smiled uncertainly.

"Trouble?"

"Automotive," he shrugged, "It's always something. They're starting to produce a new product and it's keeping them busy. In any case, he said I should show you around."

"I'd appreciate that," she nodded. She had come alone this time, to take the time to think during the long drive.

"You're from the computer firm, is that right?"

"We're working on the procurement system, yes."

"Aye. Your guys are doing good work—our system was such a mess. When we got taken over we tried for an upgrade, but of course they said no."

"No investment, right?" she asked, fishing.

"Well ... not exactly," Barton hesitated, probably wondering if he was revealing too much. "No investment yet, for sure. Typical Ward. Said he wanted to understand the problem first and then we would see. The idea is to see what we can do before we take a big leap."

"Small steps?"

"Small steps every day ... I see you've got the idea. They drive us crazy with that. Oh well, to each his own. He said I should take you to see a good example of visual management."

"I'd appreciate it, thank you."

Barton fell silent as they walked through the administrative section leading to the shop floor, and Delaney hesitated how far to push. In the end she decided that she might as well go for it.

"What's it like then, working for Ward?"

He looked at her with raised eyebrows, and then gave a reluctant, thin-lipped grin.

"Weird, that's what. Very different from the previous lot."

"How so?"

"Well now, we had a bit of a rough start when they first purchased us. Came off all preachy about this teamwork and kaizen and respect stuff. Everyone here's been in the industry forever so we've seen every possible fad come and go. We just kept our heads down and waited for it to go away."

He fell silent again and she resisted the impulse to budge him.

"But in the end, over the past year or so, I think we're learning to work together. As I said, it's weird. They completely steamrolled us with this visual management stuff: wall-to-wall, and they wouldn't take no for an answer. The red bins, the parts boards, and all the kanban stuff. We just had to do it."

"Red bins?"

"I'll show you. In any case, they were very dictatorial about it. The CEO just laid down the law. 'Get with it or get out,' he said. That and the kaizen workshops."

"The CEO's been here?"

"Jenkinson? Sure, he's been here more than a couple of times."

"What's he like?"

"American. Big chap. Very quiet. Spends most of his time in engineering, not at all the kind of Chief Exec we knew. He walks through the plant every time he's over, and always does the same thing. First he wants to see where we've had the last accident. Then he walks the flow from shipping to the materials and component warehouse. Next he'll want to see our last kaizen. Never says much, other than driving us crazy with his 'why?' and 'why?' and 'why?'"

"Seriously?"

"Yup. He's got the guys in engineering all sweating and trembling when he's over. He drills down to a level of detail that's plain scary, and he knows his stuff. To be honest, I don't act so proud when he looks at my budget either—seems he knows my numbers better than I do."

"Sounds like micromanagement."

"Well you might think that. But ... no, I wouldn't say so," he hesitated. "That's the weird part. Neither Jenkinson nor Ward ever tells us what to do. We've got a lot of rope to hang ourselves—and I mean a lot.

"They were right bullies with the visual management. And God help you if something is out of place in the plant when Jenkinson visits. But other than saying no to any new investment, they pretty much let us decide everything else—and I mean everything. And then they keep questioning what we do."

"Asking, why?" she asked.

"Aye. Why?" he rolled his eyes. "What is the problem you're trying to solve? Why? Is this the right problem? Why do you think that? Have you tried? Have you confirmed? It's endless."

"I can see how this would be uncomfortable."

"Some get used to it, some don't. We've had a couple of good guys leave the company because they felt they were being treated like school kids. But on the whole, you get used to it, and it's nice to get some autonomy back."

"Does it work?"

"Hard to know," he shrugged again with a grimace. "The factory feels like it's below par all the time with all these problems cropping up, but our results are better than they've ever been. We must be doing something right," he added with another thin smile.

"Better be lucky than good I always say. It's more stable all around, for sure, and we have a lot less corporate crap to deal with—not enough people at corporate to invent work for us now. We just work. Hang on, here we are, let me grab the supervisor."

Barton buttonholed a short, older gentleman, who introduced himself as Stevey. Barton asked him to tell Jane about his work.

"'What have you done for the operators today?' is the first thing Mr. Ward always asks me when we meet," Stevey started.

"He'd get me to solve all their personal problems as well if I listened to him," he chuckled. "But our real breakthrough moment was the red bin. As you can see in the cell, there is a red plastic bin next to each machine. When any of the workers has a doubt about whether a part is good or not, they put it into the bin and call the team leader. Because we're working one-piece-flow, this stops the cell."

"Which could make you late on the parts board, right?" Jane asked.

"Right. So the team leader, that gentleman over there," Stevey continued, pointing to one of the operators working the final station in the cell, "comes over and checks if the part is okay, and he checks how the machine works or how the operator follows the procedure. Now, either the problem can be fixed right there and then and they start again, or there's something bigger and they call me."

"You mean production remains stopped?"

"Yep. So I'd better come running, haven't I?" he chuckled again—he had that 'wise old bird' chuckle down pat. "What would be the point of continuing to build bad parts?"

"And you do this across the plant?" she asked Barton, who was standing aside not saying a word.

"Ah, not yet. Stevey here has really got the drill, but not all of the others are there yet."

"It's quite simple, really," frowned the older man. "You've got to make the difference between normal and abnormal easy to see—make it obvious. The way we came to think about this is like driving. You need a white line so that you can tell at a glance whether you're on the right side of the road or not. Our red bins keep us honest about driving straight and true.

"But it's more than knowing when problems pop up. You've got to react quickly to any abnormality. You can't continue as if nothing has happened. You can drive on the wrong side of the road, nothing's stopping you, but sooner or later you'll run into a truck. So it's all about making the cell safe and intuitive for operators, nothing more."

As he talked, Stevey was standing in front of a large board. It looked exactly like the board she saw in the other cell the last time she visited the plant, except that this one was meticulously filled in.

"Look over here," Stevey said. "First, we've got the kanban cards. Each of these cards is a production order. By looking at the queue, the team knows what it's going to make in the next couple of hours. It's just like in a restaurant: logistics gives us the orders we've got to serve in the dining hall, we put them in the order they come in on this waiting line here, and we just make them one-by-one."

"Jenkinson and Ward had us accelerate our flows radically," interjected Barton, "by getting us to level and pull our production flows with this kanban card system. It had a dramatic impact on our inventory level."

"What it really meant for us grunts on the shop floor was a stuff-load of problems," Stevey grumbled. "See, we can't fiddle with the order of the cards any longer like we used to do with our computerized production orders. We need to make the required quantity of parts when and as the card requests it. So we had to really improve our production changeovers and solve a million problems. It's all about now! No more setting one issue aside and making another part instead. Y'see?"

"Um, yes," Jane replied.

"On the other hand, it's been a blessing not to have to look into the blasted computer any more to know what we're doing. We just follow the cards. And we've got the red bins to tell us whether we're making good parts or not. At the moment, I expect to still see one or two bad parts per shift, but when we started the bins just filled up. We never knew we were making such crap! And with the parts board here, we can tell if we're driving fast enough or not. That's all there is to it. Everything is clearly displayed. And the chaps can work steadily without being constantly interrupted. It puts them in good cheer, and if they're happy so am I."

"But you must have some interruptions. I can see you've got a lot of comments written on the board." Jane observed.

"Ah, that's the good part, y'see. I come once every hour or so to see what they've written on the board. I tell them that if they don't write it down, I'm not even listening; if they don't write anything down they haven't got anything to say to me."

"And?"

"You wouldn't believe the productivity improvements!" he exclaimed. "At first, we didn't realize how many reworked parts we had and how badly they were eating our numbers. Then we had a whole load of ergonomics problems to deal with. People would slow down at the end of the shift because they got tired, or their arms and shoulders hurt with certain movements, and so on. So we sorted that out. They're switching stations every two hours to break the repetitiveness. It's still not perfect, but it's better. Now we're dealing with a lot of equipment instability.

"It's like Mr. Ward says:
  - first motion kaizen for the workers
  - then machine kaizen
  - then process kaizen to smooth the flow between machines."

"Wow. It sounds like you're doing an incredible job."

"Incredible, I don't know," he shook his head. "It's just work, innit? It's step-by-step hard work. But it's interesting. When Mr. Ward first came over, I thought his teamwork stuff was so much malarkey. I'd heard it all before, y'see. But then he made us work on his visual management ideas and suddenly it all came together. I saw how my operators could work as teams, as they do now. They work continuously and when they have a problem they stop. So it's continuous flow, stop, continuous flow, stop."

"Continuous flow, then stop," she nodded, fascinated.

"What matters is having a way to see how we work, and a way to make it better. The kicker for us was that as we solved our own problems, we realized that many of the issues we encountered came from other departments. Logistics wouldn't deliver components on time. Or maintenance would never show up—the usual, really. We'd been working like this for years."

"And? What did you do?"

"Mr. Ward told me to go for it, see?"

"Go for it?"

"Yeah, to go ahead and be a busybody and he'd support me. Said that teamwork was all about individual responsibility."

"Pardon?"

"Ar, didn't understand it meself at first. He said I should tackle one problem after the other, and organize problem-solving groups with whomever I'd want. He said that teamwork was about me learning to solve my problems with logistics or maintenance."

"And how did that go?"

"Not a walk in the park, I can tell you," he said, smiling wickedly. "I'm just a supervisor here, so they all told me to go and play up me own end. I'd set up work sessions and they wouldn't show up—same old, same old. But then Mr. Ward put the fear of God into them. And things went better. He also gave me a hard time about needing to work better with the other department heads. It's been an interesting year, that's all that I can say," he chuckled again.

Jane nodded, impressed. She also noticed that the plant manager was standing by quietly and not getting involved in the conversation. She suddenly remembered Andy's comments about still having a lot of teaching to do.

But she'd learned something. He had talked about seeing together, knowing together, and therefore acting together, but she hadn't realized that visual management was a support for teamwork. Now she could see that by creating a visual environment, he was setting up the conditions for his people to work with each other. It gave them a concrete starting point for their problem solving—they could all see the obvious, physical, abnormal situation. She glimpsed what Andy had said about using the shop floor to get people to agree on the problem before they jumped to their pet solution. In this way, functional experts could come together to solve complex problems as a team, because they could actually see the same stuff together.

"This visual stuff is very impressive," she said. "I can see that Mr. Ward puts a lot of stock in it."

"That's all he does," Stevey concurred. "He checks the visual management and looks at what problems are coming up and what problems we're focusing on. Then he looks into how we solve the problems. If we're really stuck on something, he finds someone to help us with it."

"Don't forget individual responsibility," added Barton. "We got very confused at first with the teamwork language because we'd been talking the talk about how there's no 'I' in the word team, and so on forever. But Andy taught us is that teamwork is really *individual responsibility to solve problems with our colleagues.* This is something that every one of us is supposed to do, not participate in. That's a whole different kettle of fish. Here, since this interests you, let me show you something else."

————

"I'm impressed with the enthusiasm," she said to Barton, as he took her back upstairs toward the engineering section.

"Stevey? It's a miracle, that's what it is. He was one of our most negative supervisors, a real pain the neck."

"What happened?"

"He's taken well to the problem solving. And Ward has a soft spot for him. It's not earned him a lot of friends, but whatever our Stevey asks for he gets. The one good thing that happened is that the guy is close to retirement and he's been in this plant for most of his life. When we learned we were sold, we all thought they would shut us down like all the other plants around here, but then it turned out that they meant to keep us going. Now it's nice to see old-timers like Stevey pouring their heart into their work."

"But does it pay?"

Barton gave a deep sigh.

"If you could apply the performance from Stevey's area across the plant it would—no doubt about it—but he's unfortunately an outlier. One of the reasons it works is he's got a small assembly area that he knows like the back of his hand. The heart of the plant is the press shop, and I'll confess that I'm struggling to get any traction there. We've been so used to being told to do this and do that, to apply this best practice or that one, that thinking for oneself doesn't come easy to most of the guys. But Ward seems confident that if we continue with the kaizen workshops and training programs things will improve, but I have to admit I have my doubts.

"Kaizen workshops?" Delaney prompted. "You mentioned that before but I'm unclear …"

"Ah, well," he hesitated. "Kaizen means small step improvement, so any small improvement counts as 'kaizen' in their eyes, as far as I gather. What Andy and Jenkinson are really after is spontaneous kaizen, such as operator suggestions or quality circles—you know, what we talked about in the eighties, operators spontaneously getting together to solve work issues."

"Yeah," she scoffed, "I remember hearing about those. That didn't work too well back then, did it?"

"My feeling exactly," he sighed. "But they're keen on it and they're the bosses. Anyhow, to get what they call the 'kaizen spirit' started, they ask us to lead some kaizen activities in workshop format. The idea is for managers to lead by example and step in and work with people to improve an area or fix a problem. This can happen over a few days in a workshop or longer on bigger projects."

"How do you scope them?" Jane asked.

"It really depends. Overall the methodology is:

1. We select an area for improvement. This in itself is far from simple. Andy's instructions are that we should pick an area where we have something to learn—whatever that means.

2. We find a person to lead the improvement and gather a team —preferably from various departments to develop a cross-functional perspective.

3. We look into the main components of the problem and ask each person of the team to focus specifically on one.

4. We go into an intense observation period on the shop floor. I've come to understand to a large extent that what Andy and Jenkinson are after is the observation itself. They keep saying 'observation, discussion.'

5. The team leader tracks each person's observations, challenges them to carry things further, and to try things right away.

6. The leader then meets with everyone to discuss the findings and the changes implemented, first individually and then as a team.

7. The leader then posts the results in a common area to get further input, and to continue to track and support further ongoing work to stabilize the improvements."

"Wow. You're expected to improve things right away?"

"On the spot. If it's not too risky or costly. And, yes, it can be brutal. But we do learn a lot, though I have to say, I keep being caught off guard by what Andy finds interesting and worth pursuing— or not."

"Oh, I know the feeling," Delaney muttered.

"Ah, and here we are: my own torture board," said Barton, as he and Jane stepped into a conference room with papers pasted across all the walls.

"Development projects?" she asked, recognizing the similarity with her own war room back at Southcape.

"Manufacturing engineering. Ward's come up with this rule that the plant can only absorb one new product at a time, which has been a real relief. What we have here are the engineering projects in the pipeline. We meet regularly with the supervisors so that everyone understands what's coming down."

"Teamwork?"

"When it's not a bloodbath, yes. Here's the board I wanted to show you." The site manager pointed to a large whiteboard with three columns: new, current, closed—with a grapple of Post-its on the current column and a few in the closed one.

"Ward asked me to pick one cross-functional problem—sales, engineering, production, purchasing, the lot—every fortnight. The idea is to focus on difficulties we have working together."

"Every two weeks?"

"We tried to do it weekly, but even twice a month we struggle."

"Let me see if I understand: you guys focus on a new cross-functional problem every two weeks, and then you have to solve it?"

"Not me. I pick someone in the management team and they have to solve it. The board is used to check whether we're progressing fast enough. As you can see, most get stuck in the 'current' column."

"You mentioned this already, individual responsibility, right? One person is responsible to solve the problem."

"Yes, by working with the others, that's Jenkinson and Andy's way. This is what they call teamwork. It's not a free-for-all. It took me almost a year to understand that what they saw in teamwork was individual development."

"It does sound weird," she admitted.

"They don't believe in collective learning," he said. "They keep saying, 'only *individuals* learn.' What they're aiming for is teaching every one to work better with each other. So one person is clearly responsible to solve the problem, but they have to work with specified colleagues—they're not supposed to go off and do it on their own."

"What happens if they don't get on?"

"Welcome to my world," he said mournfully. "We used to get along fine—as long as every one did their own thing. But now they've got us working on topics together all the time It's not always sweetness and light. My job is to keep all the issues on the board moving and to help whoever's stuck to move forward. As you can see, I'm not doing that well, but it's better than it used to be."

"It's about getting the whole company working as one team, isn't it?"

"So they say. They use this analogy of a rowing race. If you've got four rowers on each side but they can't row together, the boat will zigzag wildly. If one rower feels he's stronger than the others and rows harder, he'll upset the boat and row it off course. The idea is that each of us has to learn to row evenly, at the same depth and time as the others. They believe that this sort of teamwork is not just the key to success, but an acquirable skill. It's hard to dispute their logic, but the practice of it is *tough*!"

"Like an orchestra."

"Or a sports team. Yes. It's *really* not easy. First we've got to learn to communicate, not just talk past one another. Then we've got to learn to trust each other. All that 'respect' stuff forces us to make a genuine effort to understand each other's point of view. It gets better as we do resolve issues, but old habits die hard. According to Ward, it starts with this board."

"Thanks you for showing me this," she said thoughtfully. "I must chew on it."

"You're welcome. He asked me to explain this visual board specifically. Thought it'd apply to you somehow."

"I wonder what would have given him that idea," she said with a sudden laugh.

———

"Jane? Are you in?" her assistant called over the intercom. "I've got Mr. Bainbridge on the line."

She took a deep, grounding breath. Lionel Bainbridge was the partner in charge of Southcape at the private equity firm: a pure financier, impeccably polite, and trustworthy as a snake.

"Patch him in, Ally. Thanks."

"Lionel," she said with as much pleasure as she could muster. "Good to hear you. What can I do for you?"

"Oh, nothing specific, just a catch up really ... this and that."

"Anything specific?"

"Well, there is one small thing. Your latest forecast has us somewhat worried. Profitability doesn't look too good, does it?"

"We're aware of it, Lionel. We're working on it."

"But with this newest lost contract, we worry ...?"

"Lost contract?" she repeated.

"Haven't you lost the … er … MRX deal?"

"Not that I know," she said, caught off guard. "We were up for renewal, but the decision shouldn't be in for another week or two, as far as I know."

"Ah. I'm so sorry. I must have been confused with the dates. Apologies and all that."

"No worries, if you do hear something definite, please let me know," she said calmly.

"Of course, of course. Not that I'm likely to. Well, it's been real good talking to you."

"Likewise, Lionel, likewise."

"You will pass along that action plan you mentioned? About the profitability recovery, yes?"

"As soon as it's finished, absolutely. Without fault."

"Splendid, then. Splendid."

"Good night, Lionel. Talk to you soon."

––––––––––––

What was that about?, she wondered furiously. What the hell could have happened with MRX that the vampires heard about it before she did. The worst possible thing for any exec was when people around you knew things before you did. She fought off a wave of panic. Ward had warned her that things would get worse before they got better. Well, they just had.

The MRX relationship was a real shambles. Simon Burnsell had jumped ship and joined the client company, arguing that he could do the job by himself better over there. More surprisingly, he'd taken young Ryan Cox with him—she never thought those two got along particularly well.

She'd called the IT director and finally persuaded him that it made sense to for them to create their own implementation team ("yes, yes, apology accepted, it's better like this all around"). But that they probably didn't have enough resources yet no matter how brilliant Simon was ("yes, yes, he's very good, and so is Ryan"—and I hate your guts you dirty poaching bastard) to do all the work that needed to be done. He agreed to postpone any immediate decision before they'd had time to jointly review the project.

It was iffy, but the man had sounded pleasant on the phone and not given any impression that they were about to shut them out. But who knew? Now she needed to find out how the information had gone so fast to Bainbridge. She couldn't help thinking it was pure Rob maneuvering ... but enough for one day.

———

The first-floor window lights were on when she finally arrived home. Sara was in her room again, in the middle of the week.

"Hello, my sweet," she said softly, walking into her daughter's room to kiss her goodnight. She was crouched over her computer, her face backlit by the screen, writing an essay, or on Facebook. "You're home again?"

"Hi, Mom," Sara said without looking up.

"You know, I worry when you drive back at night like this," Jane said, sitting down on her daughter's bed. "It's a long drive."

"Oh, I'm fine."

"What's wrong with the dorm? I thought you got on well with your roommate."

"I do."

The silence grew and filled the space between them, as solid as a wall, and Jane winced, feeling more shut out than ever.

"Do you want to talk about it?" she finally said lamely.

Her daughter mumbled something.

"What?"

"What's the point? You never listen."

Jane forced herself to stay very still.

"I'm listening now. I thought you liked Jo."

"She's a friend," her daughter replied weakly.

"What's up then, pumpkin?"

"There's this boy," she said huffily.

"And you like him?"

"What? No! Eeek, he's a creep."

"Oh."

"But Jo really likes him. Like, *really*."

The wheels whirred and clicked.

"And sometimes, he stays over?"

Her daughter shrugged again, looking at her screen more intensely than ever. Jane didn't say anything, just watched her daughter, thinking of how beautiful she'd become.

"I know, I know," Sara finally said. "You're going to tell me that I have to deal with the problem and face up to Jo. But she's my *friend*."

"Oh, sweetheart," Jane said, feeling so weak inside that if the slightest wind had blown in the room she'd have been torn apart like paper cuttings. "I was going to say nothing of the sort. This is your home. You'll always be safe and warm here. Come home as often as you want. Just be careful on the road."

"Mother!" said the girl getting up from her chair and moving close to her, wrapping her arms around her shoulders.

Stand in their shoes, look through their eyes.

Damn it! She thought wearily. Problems first. Why did it have to be so *hard*?

Chapter Four

INVOLVE EVERYONE
IN IMPROVEMENT

"Can't do it, I'm sorry," said Mike Wembley.

"Can't? Or won't?"

"Can't, Janey. I'm not being difficult. We're just not good enough."

"Talk me through it," Jane urged, as she motioned the waiter that they were ready to order.

Alyson, her assistant, had worked a minor miracle, scheduling lunch with Mike on Wednesdays for the past couple of weeks. Rob had showed up for one awkward lunch and then failed to come again, not even bothering to make excuses. That day the three of them had tried to discuss the company's current state, but could not agree on anything—not even on basic problems to tackle. Rob had been full of advice on how to improve operations but would not even consider that Sales could be part of the problem. She was at her wits' end about how to address that relationship. But tackling that problem would simply have to come later.

She was happy to be working closely with Mike once more. His mind didn't work like others. She had learned a great deal from him about a range of topics, including the future of computing. He saw software as something people experienced, not just clever tools they used. As she gradually moved away from staring at screens into to her role as CEO she had come to see talk like this as over-intelligent hot air. But lately, as she continued to visit clients and forced herself to understand their perspective, she was more open to the idea of user experience.

"First," said Mike, "I gathered together a small group of interested developers from across the firm. I explained the situation and asked them to build tests as they coded. The idea was that I'd check up on them to see how they were doing."

"Who are we talking about?"

"The chaps you call the T-shirt brigade," he laughed. "Chris Williamson, Terry Boyle, Charlotte Happer. The kids mostly, those who still dream they'll grow up to be Larry and Sergei."

She nodded, smiling. "And?"

"Failed. With the exception of Boyle, who's got some real attitude issues but is very good. They all tried, got bogged down, and eventually stopped trying."

"Why?"

"Honestly? They're not good enough. Plain and simple, they don't know how to develop their own tests. Furthermore, when they do their code crashes all the time because of the tests, and they get impatient with that. So they stop and hope it'll build and that the biggest bugs will be caught later."

"Hmm. I have recently noticed in my various tours that getting folks to stop and deal with problems in 'real-time' is a huge mental shift—that it doesn't come easily in any setting," Jane shared.

"So I changed tack and took Charlotte and Daniela out of the process to create a small task force."

"Daniela? But who's testing the Nexplas code?"

"Tut-tut!" clucked Mike. "Carte blanche you said," he reminded her in a faux French accent. She nodded, making a mental note to check on the Nexplas project.

"Now, the idea is that Daniela and Charlotte schedule time with the coders to teach them how to develop automated testing. The coders bitch about it, but they're not going to say no to me, are they?"

"And?" she wondered, anxiously.

"Not only do they find it hard to grasp, but we're discovering real competence concerns, particularly in the people we've hired the last couple of years. I also found out that the code reviews we used to do have more or less gone by the wayside. The pressure is on to deliver—nobody worries much about anything else."

"Hence the re-releases …"

"Partly that; partly spec misunderstandings between sales and project leaders. That's also glaringly obvious."

"Agreed. I'd picked up on this myself, but don't know how to take it up with Rob. I can't wake up someone who's pretending to sleep."

"Um. Yes, well … on the testing front, I don't think it makes sense to continue. We'll never get to a self-testing culture if we don't deal with some of our deeper competence issues first."

"Oh, please, Mike," she begged. "Please don't give up. I hear what you're saying about competence, I really do. But I need time to think about it. Consider this: we wouldn't even be having this conversation if you hadn't done the work. So hang on in there. My hunch is we *really* need this."

He perked up slightly. "There is one teeny-weeny ray of sunlight, I do have something fun to show you. It's back at the office."

———

Back at Southcape, Mike took her to the large room where a team of five people was running the continuous maintenance and development for a mainstream bank application. She had just signed the renewal of this contract, which had been a major relief. Not just for the cash flow, but also because the bank clients had been very positive about the team and the work they did—a welcome relief from all the bad news she'd been getting these days.

She went round saying hi to the team members, wondering what she was supposed to see. Mike stood in the doorway looking like a proud father. They had their project plan on the wall, as well as one of Ward's paperboards. They had established a routine where they discussed one problem a day in a stand-up meeting just before going to lunch. The project leader was a young Scot with an incomprehensible accent—you wouldn't glance at him twice on the street. She'd always found him mind-bogglingly dull, but he got on well with everybody and got the job done.

She was changing her mind about her staff, she noted, amused. Less influenced by her likes and dislikes, and better able to evaluate their sills and ability to create value. She looked around the room but couldn't tell what she was supposed to see. 'What?' she mouthed silently to Mike, who was laughing quietly.

"This gimmick," he said happily, pointing toward a flat screen with a child's Mickey Mouse lamp USB-ed to it. "Ewan, why don't you talk us through it?"

"There's nothing much to it," the young man said, looking up. "We were discussing the idea of 'stop' rather than workaround a problem—as yuh explained it to us. We talked to Mike about it and came up this thing: we code and build and run the testing on this machine. If the code crashes the mousie lights up. When that happens, we all stop what we're doing, gather up, and try an' figure out where we went wrong."

"Brilliant!" she exclaimed. "Very clever. And, your conclusions?"

"Oh, aye, hard taskmaster that beastie," he grinned. The rest of the team was laughing now, somewhat defensively. She wondered what was going on.

"At first it was nah much fun, it kept lighting up. None of us wanted to stop, we wanted to keep racing on. But we're learning fast, that's for sure. It keeps showing us the mistakes we're still making, and I dinnae see an end to it. Aaarh! Look the bluidy Mickey is flashing again."

"They've uncovered some pretty interesting coding problems," interjected Mike, as the team congregated around the testing screen. "Some in the new stuff, but a lot in the legacy of the application. I've tried to help them do some triage because they were being overwhelmed with issues."

"We set up this parking space here," Ewan went on, showing her another sheet posted on the wall. "These are the issues we've decided to live with for now, but we'll have to go back to at some point."

"What would you need to tackle those as well?" she asked him.

"Ah. That's a hard one. We'd need someone with experience of the system. It's all interconnected, so we're a bit weary of just changing stuff in there."

"Do you remember that chap we developed this with, back in the day?" she asked Wembley, annoyed that she could clearly visualize the man's face but not remember his name.

"Brian something or other?" he asked in surprise. "Sure. Why?"

"Last time I heard he was still working as a freelancer. Maybe we want him on this team?"

"He wasn't cheap," objected Mike.

"Your call, if it's money well spent I won't look at it twice," she smiled, feeling good about being the boss for the first time in days. "This is absolutely great, guys. Keep it up," she said, beaming at the team. "Draw up a list of what support you need and email it to me. In the meantime, pizzas all around! Well done team!"

––––––––––

She spotted Ward sprawled at a small table in the airport café. He was staring into mid-air and didn't see her coming until she stood right next to him. She was amused to note his crisp designer jeans, well-cut blazer, dark-gray quilted vest, and a navy blue-and-white striped shirt. This was a sign of vanity she'd not picked up in him before. She noticed with amusement that he was still wearing his battered safety shoes and she wondered how he got them through airport security.

Earlier that day he had phoned apologetically for canceling their scheduled visit right after his no-show at the plant. Because she really needed to talk to him, she offered to meet him at the airport (one benefit of Southcape's location) if he had spare time before his flight—which was thankfully delayed by poor weather conditions.

"Nice waistcoat," she commented as she sat down across the table, breaking one of the cardinal rules of being a woman in a man's corporate world: don't ever discuss clothes.

"Um … ah, yes, thank you," he smiled self-consciously. "I have a plant in Torino and, well, *mea culpa*, I've gotten a habit of shopping for clothes at Caselle Airport on the way back," he said. "My wife thinks it's a definite improvement," he added with a wide yawn.

"You look done for. Too much work?"

"Nah," he waved his hand in apology. "Baby at home. Elsa is eight months old and still wakes up at least once a night. It's driving us crazy."

"Your first?"

"Second, her older brother just turned six this month."

"One thing I like about flying," she said when she saw he wasn't going to elaborate further, "is the quiet of being in the plane where no one can reach you. And in winter we get the bonus of blue skies above the clouds. Time to be still, if you know what I mean."

"I do," he grinned. "Although it's not so much an issue for me. I live in a farmhouse in the middle of the countryside, so I get as much quiet as I can handle."

"Do you?" she asked in surprise. "How does this work out with your job? Don't you have a lot of traveling to do?"

"Not too bad, really," he yawned again, more discreetly. "I mostly do Europe. Nothing like Phil. Now that Asia's growing so fast, he's got to be everywhere at the same time. I'm about an hour and a half drive from the airport. I tend to stay at the office at the beginning and the end of the week, and then travel for the rest of the time. With spring coming, it gets much easier without all the winter hassle.

"The good thing about my job is that they don't actually need me there to run the day-to-day. As long as I visit every plant regularly and I'm available when they've got a crisis, I'm pretty free with my time. Phil's cut down on much of the corporate-driven work, the reporting, planning, and all the other usual dances, so I can work to a schedule. And the shop floor is always interesting. As Phil says, the day you tire of plant visits is the day to sell the company," he grinned.

Phil again. She swore she had to meet the man one day, if only for curiosity's sake.

"So," he said, squinting at the departure board. "How're you doing?"

"Bizarre, to say the least."

"How so?" he wondered.

"On the one hand, we're doing better. Sales have picked up a bit and a couple of big contracts have been renewed, which is a huge relief. On the other ... it's puzzling. I've been giving every project leader a hard time—and I mean a *hard* time, the 'bitch boss' thing— about listening to their customers' grievances. I've also forced them to keep doing your paperboard thing, which they hate. The upshot is that we're far more aware of what we're not doing for customers and we don't know how to fix it."

"Okay. And what's strange about this?"

"The strange thing is that we've regained two big clients we thought we had lost. They understand that we don't know how to solve all their issues, but they still signed up. As a result, turnover is back on forecast—slightly above even. And profitability is up, as well, though I'm not sure why. The numbers are looking better, but the firm has never felt like such a train wreck. We've got issues coming out of our ears, everyone is working hard treading water, and we don't seem to be making progress on anything. I don't know how long I can keep them at it."

"It's like the story of the two guys running from a lion," Andy smiled. "One of them stops to put on his running shoes and the other runs ahead saying, 'Why are you stopping? Are you crazy?' The guy answers, 'I don't have to run faster than the lion. I just have to run faster than you.' That's probably what is happening with your customers. Other providers are not likely to be much better than you. When you show respect to your customers, they respond—no mystery there."

"But we're not *fixing* anything."

"There are two sides to business," he reminded her, "results and relationships. You're fixing the relationship. And for what it's worth, I believe you're really leading the company. Visible behavior change is what leadership is all about, even if it's too early to tell whether you'll succeed. In fact, you're probably solving customer issues you simply didn't see before.

"It's the same on the profitability front. By getting people to focus on what they do and making them aware of the waste they create, in all likelihood many mistakes are being avoided and waste is being taken out your processes. It's hard to measure the cost/benefit of errors avoided, but in my experience this is huge—and the earlier in the project definition the greater the savings. So you're probably improving your profitability, although it won't appear in your numbers for a while."

"Thanks for the vote of confidence," she said, happy to hear his endorsement of her leadership. "I hear what you're saying, but it's hard to see."

Ward reached over, grabbed a napkin, and pulled out an odd-looking pen with a ballpoint on one end and a soft top on the other for drawing on touchscreens. Clearly a relic from a conference, she thought to herself. On the napkin he wrote:

- Safeguard your people
- Protect your customers
- Control your lead-time
- Reduce your lead-time
- And your costs will go down

"As I've done more and more partnerships and taken the *lead with respect* practice to more companies," he explained, "I've discovered a general arc to what happens. This has evolved to be the general action plan when I start anywhere. Things have been growing very fast these past three years, so I'm getting a lot of practice at this.

"Leading is about getting companies to reorient on these five basic activities. Lead with respect is about hearing their side of things and taking the responsibility to create the kind of relationship necessary for them to work the way you'd like. Typically, they've been brought up in a world where the true priorities are quarterly profits and monthly numbers optimization. Improving and growing people by teaching them to visualize issues and solve problems together is completely alien to them. It's your job to change that."

"I can see the protect customers part," Delaney agreed, pulling out her tablet and jotting down his list. "I do believe we're working on safeguarding our people and protecting our customers from our own screw-ups. But what do you mean by control the lead-time?"

"Make sure your projects are delivered on time. Take out the variation."

"Shouldn't we aim for reduced lead-time first? I've been having this debate with the other directors. They think that if we apply our workflow processes more rigorously and reengineer how we organize projects, we should be able to work faster and have a better chance of delivering on time ... What's so funny?"

"Nothing, nothing," he grinned. "It's a natural mistake to make, and I've learned that the hard way. Look, everyone learned about respect from Toyota. In the early years, everyone could see that Toyota had far more efficient processes with incredibly short lead times. They were building cars—from raw materials to delivery—in days when the rest of the industry was taking weeks, even months."

"Yes, I've read up on that," she nodded.

"Quite naturally, many people thought they had to learn and copy Toyota's 'best practice.' So they did. They studied how Toyota ran their factories and they scrupulously implemented what they had learned in their own operations and ..." he raised his eyes theatrically.

"And?"

"No results or small results, short-term savings, and no sustainable improvement. They created Toyota-like processes but could not cope

101

with the fundamental instabilities in the way that they worked. Real-life variation—such as bad parts and machine problems as we've seen in the Swindon shop—is covered by inventories. If you put process steps together and reduce inventories between the steps without improving your capabilities, you just get reengineered processes that don't work and overflow everywhere. So you go back to adding inventories and lengthening your lead time."

"Ahhh ..."

"Look over there," he suggested, pointing at a queue of passengers waiting at the till in the airport newsstand, where one harassed-looking cashier was dealing with an argumentative customer. "Can you spot the waste?"

"Waste, I don't know," she laughed, "but clearly, there is only one open till. And the other woman over there is restocking shelves when she could be opening the second till and serving customers, right?"

"So what would you do?"

"I'd have a process like they do in supermarkets: when the queue starts to build someone should stop restocking shelves and open the second till."

"That's precisely my point," grinned Ward. "You just reengineered the process. You looked at the situation, identified the problem, solved it by applying a solution you already know, and now what?"

"I need to train the two women to follow that process?"

"Indeed," he agreed in his most annoying cat-and-mouse tone. "But don't you think they might already have such a process in place?"

"And they might not know how to use it?" she thought out loud.

"Or feel it matters, or something else has happened, yes," he nodded. "That's the point. It's not a process issue, it's a capability issue: recognizing the situation, knowing how to resolve it, asking who is competent to open the till, and so on. Chances are one of them is qualified to hold the till and not the other, or something like it. If we design clever processes for people and machines that don't have the capability to deal with what's thrown at them, the result will be even more chaos than before."

"I was leading without respect, is that it?" she asked thoughtfully. "I was looking at the obvious waste and solution and thinking how they should apply it. I was not looking at whether the cashiers saw the problem or if they know how to deal with this specific situation. Stand in their shoes and look through their eyes again.

"Lordy!" she exclaimed in frustration. "This is such an easy trap to fall into!"

"Uh-huh," Andy agreed, "happens to me all the time. We can't help but think of a solution—this is what we do. And there's nothing wrong about that. The problem is jumping in and failing to uncover the real situation—and the point of view of the people living the issue. Lead with respect takes so much practice because it's hard to balance how much challenging one does with how much listening, how much teaching about better ways to do things with how much supporting. One thing I'm definite about is that if you try to implement 'improved processes' without building people's capabilities, you'll just create more broken processes."

She closed her eyes briefly, thinking it through. It made sense.

"So instead of reducing your costs," he continued, "you've spent a lot of money on a reengineering project without dealing with all the effects of uncontrolled variation. It might be an improvement on paper, but you won't find it in the accounts."

"We seem to have things backwards."

"Precisely," he agreed. "We're conditioned to think that processes exist in and of themselves, as a sequence of steps, involving production machines, or development, or whatever. We feel that if a process is defined well enough, human activity should be simple enough so that any idiot can do it. If the performance lags, we need to fix the process. So it makes sense to try and reduce process lead-time right away."

"But …"

"But it appears that people are never competent enough to deal with these so-called efficient processes. Nobody can cope with the discipline and rigor required to make them work. I'm not saying that good processes are not important. Certainly, even competent people can't deliver much with broken processes. The point is that processes and people are linked. To perform we need both, the best people and the best processes."

She raised her eybrows and said, "So you're saying:

PERFORMANCE = BEST PEOPLE + BEST PROCESS."

He laughed good-naturedly at her kidding. "Yes, another equation. We recently had a case with an assembly process where parts came out of a press and additional parts needed to be inserted by hand. One of our guys saw exactly the same process at a Toyota supplier; they had the insertion step in perfect one-piece-flow with the press. Having seen the better process, he decided we should do the same. Unfortunately, our pressing process was not good enough and we had to deburr many parts before adding the inserts. Also the process had many instabilities, which meant that on average it took longer than planned to insert components.

"As a result, parts accumulated between the press and the insertion station with no place to put them. We found them everywhere around the cell—on the floor, underneath the conveyor, everywhere. They stacked the iffy parts, deburred them offline, and placed them back in the flow. It was a complete mess!

"We had to teach the engineers that before we could handle a one-piece-flow process with no parts between pressing and insertion, we first had to improve injection precision and insertion capability. In the meantime, they had better keep a buffer, and pull parts from pressing to insertion. As we say in lean, flow when you can, pull when you can't. In this case, we were simply not good enough to flow as the Toyota supplier did, so we had to pull."

"Is that what's happening to us?" Jane wondered. "When we actually looked at our lead-time performance, we realized that our people are not good enough? That's certainly the impression we have."

"In all likelihood, yes. This is why you need to control process lead-time, by stabilizing every step before you try to reduce it, and certainly before you change the control logic in the process."

"So hold on," said Jane, thinking. "You're saying that variation in the process lead-time reflects gaps in our competence level?"

"Absolutely. Variation occurs because someone, somewhere, made a mistake or an inappropriate decision, mostly without ever realizing they were doing so."

"Which is why you're so keen on making mistakes visible ..."

"Yes. And it's important to remember that the value of seeing mistakes is not about punishing individuals but about understanding how systems create errors. It's vital that leadership's attitude must always be that operators—or programmers—are *not guilty*!" he said, raising a finger.

"But what happens when somebody screws up? It happens, surely?"

"Sure, all the time."

"Don't they get blamed?"

"Not guilty!"

"But if they were lazy and ..."

"Not guilty!"

"Or they willfully did something wrong ..."

"Not guilty!"

"Okay, I get what you're saying! But please clarify what you mean."

"We're militant about *not guilty*. Lead with respect means that the employee is not guilty, and that's that."

"Even when they actually screwed up?" she asked, incredulously.

"Well, we have a problem if we say '*guilty*!' First, we need to create a workplace where people *want* to reveal their mistakes. They'll never do this if they fear they'll be put on the spot. Secondly, not all screw-ups are bad."

"I don't get it."

"We're trying to get people to solve problems and try new things all the time. It doesn't always work the first time. Actually, it rarely works the first time. So we need to create an environment in which failure is okay, in which people are not guilty."

"How can failure be okay?" she huffed.

"There are different kinds of failures. There are good failures: you tried something that didn't work out the way you'd thought. And there are bad failures: you did something that was just plain dumb. The problem is, it's often hard to distinguish the good failures from the bad ones upfront, and if we start punishing the bad failures, we're likely to drive out innovation. Like I said long ago, the phrase we use is: 'Ask why, not who?'"

"This is going to take some getting used to," she grumbled.

"It's a …"

"Practice. I know. I get it. I need to practice *not guilty*—on top of everything else."

"We all need to practice *not guilty*—the blaming, knee-jerk reaction is hard to fight."

"But then if performance is not driven by the process but instead by people's competence, and if people are not guilty—where does that leave us? What's the answer?"

"Are you ready for the answer?" he replied in a mock deep tone.

"There's an answer?"

"There is, but I want to know that you're truly ready for it."

"Sure. What is it?"

"You're not going to like it," he said playfully, continuing to yank her chain.

"What?" she growled in mock exasperation.

"It's all about people!" he said with a smile.

"That's it?"

"There's nothing else," he said, with an open-handed gesture.

"It's *all* about people," he continued. "We've come to see processes as what people *do*. From the lead with respect perspective, people make products or deliver services; machines and software are there to support them, but never to dominate them. People build products, and better thinking by those people builds better products."

"That's exactly what our founder used to say!" she exclaimed. "Almost word for word: great people make great software."

"Wise man. There you go. Great people make great products."

"But where does that leave us?"

"You hit it right on the nail with your equation: better processes and better people create better performance. To improve performance we have to improve processes. To improve processes we have to improve individual's competence and their ability to work with others.

"That's how lead with respect delivers outstanding results," he continued, excitedly. "If your people are better at what they do the processes they come up with can't be copied by your competition— it's an enduring competitive advantage. Your competitors won't be able to keep up with your pace of improvement."

"They'll never catch up, as long as they try to improve the process but not the people," she concluded thoughtfully. "I can see the logic of it, but to be honest it doesn't help me much. I've been fighting with everything and everyone to visualize what we do and reveal mistakes, but so far I haven't got a clue about how to improve competencies. What's the answer to that?"

"Problem solving," he said simply. "Teaching people to solve their own problems."

"Problem solving?" she repeated.

"Yep. The issue is not people in general, but people as individuals. First we need them to see the waste they cause to others by the choices they make. We're all very sensitive to the waste others cause us, but seeing the waste that we cause others takes a concerted effort. Competence is about understanding how our choices generate waste in other parts of the process."

"Respect again? Making an effort to understand the waste we cause to others?"

"Absolutely. It's like the woman over there. She doesn't realize that by choosing to restock the shelves while angry customers are waiting, she is slowing down sales and seriously damaging the brand." He picked up another napkin and continued. "In order to develop individual competence, every employee needs to be taught to:

1. Know their job in detail, step by step.
2. Recognize the waste they generate by their choices.
3. Express the problems precisely and seek root causes.
4. Study the countermeasures.
5. Learn to work better with their colleagues.

"In doing so they deepen their technical expertise and their understanding of their job," Ward said.

Jane worked this out and copied it down on her tablet. "That's what they tried to tell me in the plant. Practice again."

"Indeed, learning by doing," he nodded.

"Takes forever?"

"No magic bullet, I'm afraid," he grinned in acknowledgement. "And it must continue forever. The moment you stop, the rubber band snaps back and you're back exactly where you started."

"And that's all there is?" she said, shaking her head in disbelief.

"There's always more," he laughed.

"Well, it seems that you have plenty of time to enlighten me," she said wryly. "Isn't that your flight delayed because of late arrival of the incoming aircraft?"

"Dammit! You're right," he answered crestfallen. "Heathrow is not as bad as Roissy for flight delays, but in winter it's pretty dire."

"I'd like to continue with this," she said. "Unless you've got other work to do."

"No, no," he sighed. "This is an important topic. If you're okay with time, I'm fine."

"Great. But first I'm going to get something to drink," she said, standing up. "What do you fancy?"

"Coffee would be lovely."

"Right away," she smiled to herself, as she broke another of her business rules: never be the one to get the coffee.

As she moved away, Andy checked his phone for messages and grumbled to himself about the delayed flight. For once, though, he couldn't consider the hold-up wasted time. It was much harder than he'd expected to explain lead with respect. Talking with Jane was forcing him to clarify his own thinking. As he recalled his difficulties with Len Barton and his gang, he wondered whether he should spend more time talking with them.

Maybe he had to rethink his whole approach at the Swindon plant. For some reason, they didn't resist but they didn't buy in. As a result, they either kept doing what he asked just to please him or to get him off their backs, but they did not learn the deeper lessons underneath. The outcome was a lot of "pretend lean," which set his teeth on edge. But it was difficult to counter, as he could not blame them for not doing something.

Working with Jane was refreshing and the complete opposite of Barton. He'd never experienced any one both confident to ask the hard questions and keen to understand the answers—and not afraid to try things on her own.

In this unique situation, the 'teach versus support' balance was unexpectedly tilted toward teach—he gave her very little support. This was different from what he did most of the time, where he taught less and supported more: encouraging people to try things, pushing them to look at other options, biting his tongue not to blame them when they made mistakes, making sure they weren't making costly ones, and so on.

Maybe the problem with Swindon was him. He'd definitely not found the right way to get through to them, which was ironic. A case of no one is a prophet in his own land, maybe. Perhaps the issue was precisely that the management style he'd developed in France, Germany, Poland, and Italy grated here in his home country … In any case, talking to Jane had opened up a different chain of thoughts.

———————

Delaney returned to the table and handed Ward a large Styrofoam cup of coffee. He thanked her and began warming his hands over the steaming black liquid.

"Let's see, where were we? Oh, yes, people and processes," Andy summarized. "We agree then that in order to achieve our business objectives, we need to improve our processes. And in order to improve processes, we need to improve our people."

"Yes, I'm with you so far," she said.

"Well, my CEO and I use a T-development model to visualize people development. You need to develop every one of your employees in two dimensions: first in the technical expertise of their job, that should be obvious. And second in their leadership ability, the ability to work with their colleagues downstream (internal and external customers) and upstream (internal and external suppliers).

"When I look at someone in my organization I trust them to do their day-to-day job well enough, but I worry about the kaizen part of JOB = WORK + KAIZEN.

"Take Nina Miah, for instance. You've met her. She's the woman in charge of procurement at Swindon."

"Our client, yes."

"One of the urgent issues we had to solve at Swindon when we acquired it was the poor quality of delivery from their suppliers, which led to frequent stoppages or rescheduling on the assembly lines when parts were lacking."

T-development Model

Leadership: Solving problems with upstream and downstream colleagues

Expertise: Better understanding the fundamentals of the job, and knowing how to deal correctly with specific cases

"Variation in the process."

"That's right, variation. Poor quality was probably our number one source of variation. And for Nina, the first step was realizing that most part shortages—despite large inventories—were created by her own supply method. The shortages were generated by what she was asking her procurement operators to do."

"The problem is you," grinned Jane.

"We make our own misery," Andy laughed. "I had her plot the variation from one order to the next at our main suppliers. She discovered that one day we'd ask for four crates, another for 40, and so forth. The supplier would ship whatever they had in stock and reschedule the rest for production. Sometimes we received too much, other times too little. When she graphed this variation the result was so jagged that you would never have guessed that our production schedule was actually pretty level. This visualization exercise finally got her to understand," he said, shaking his head in bewilderment or vexation. "Nothing is ever easy."

"Is that how we got involved in sorting out your parts ordering process?" she asked.

"Later on, yeah. First, Nina had to accept that the goalpost had moved and change her thinking about how she did her job. She had misinterpreted just-in-time, thinking that it was about getting the supplier to deliver whatever she wanted whenever she wanted it. In other words, it was the supplier's problem. But just-in-time is really about reducing lead-time. She had to learn how to make it easier for suppliers to deliver on time.

"This meant stabilizing orders to the suppliers so that they could produce and ship according to a stable plan, rather than being constantly barraged by erratic orders. Rather than just follow the Materials Requirement Planning (MRP) system, her procurement team had to learn to level demand to suppliers—sometimes by hand. The new goal was to avoid any last-minute surprise orders: don't catch the supplier out with an order he can't fulfill.

"It wasn't easy, but as Nina changed her mind, she learned. Her supplier performance increased, which reduced the chaos in the plant considerably. In order to do that, she had to get the hang of many things she simply didn't know how to do with the existing IT system. That's when we called in your guys."

"It also explains why we didn't understand what you wanted," Delaney said. "You were not looking for a system upgrade. You were looking to learn, right?" She couldn't help but note to herself that it would have helped if he had just said that at the time.

"At that time, yes," Ward said. "I'm not sure where this issue stands now and things could change. But yes, we needed to modify the MRP logic to help visualize variation for the procurement operators, so that they could learn how to order better from their suppliers. This meant breaking away from the old MRP formula that favored ordering in large batches. The purchasing people are now the driver. The software must support them."

"As opposed to placing people in a system that does everything on its own with limited human input. I'm starting to get it, but it does turn IT on its head." She paused. "The funny part is that that's how we started Southcape—creating systems for people to use on their PCs to solve their own problems."

"Uh-huh. That's the vertical part of the T-model. Nina and her team developed an expertise they didn't have before by solving the specific problem of leveling the orders to suppliers. As a result they changed their process, and with your chaps' help they started developing new tools to support the improved process.

"Now, I've done this many times before in other plants. But what do you think would have happened if I'd come in all guns blazing and imposed the new process on them?"

"They'd have resisted it. 'Not invented here,' and so on."

"And not understood what I was after. We got lucky because a few of the things your team did for us were really clever—and better than what I've gotten at other sites. Now we need to study the counter-measures more deeply to figure out what they did cleverly and what ideas we could spread back across the company.

"I never realized," admitted Delaney, taken aback.

Ward looked up and checked the departures board. He sighed as he saw that his flight was still delayed indefinitely. "I may be here awhile. Might as well continue.

"The horizontal side of the T-development model is leadership. Nina realized that she couldn't do the job properly in isolation, because procurement was linked to sales administration and planning. Back when she was just following the system's instructions and replenishing orders according to the MRP's stock figures, she never really needed to interact with the downstream part of the process. But now that she was trying to level and accelerate the procurement flow, the needs of production became critical.

"Of course, the planning department was another big mess ... dedicated to dealing with all the rescheduling and changes. We were implementing kanban in the factory, which meant that we imposed a leveled production plan for all high-running parts. No one in planning really wanted to think what this meant, so Nina took it up.

She worked closely with Tim on logistics and one of the younger planners, to understand what we needed to get the kanban working. Since she was part of the management team, she could get things done. And this is what essentially freed Tim to perform miracles."

"And strengthened her leadership role."

"Precisely. Len Barton, the guy you met, is a great technical guy but he's got no feel for logistics, which isn't surprising since the MRP ran things in the past. Now, if I can just get the two of them to work together well I've solved a huge part of my equation!"

"Teamwork again," she noted, "and across boundaries, as well."

"Lead with respect. It starts by making an effort to understand each other, taking responsibility to do your best to build trust and teamwork, and supporting individual development to maximize team performance. Process performance is an outcome, not an input."

"It turns everything I've ever learned about management upside down," she said after a moment of quiet. "Or inside out," she smiled. "It's radical!"

"It works for us! We've got double the growth and double the profitability of any company in our industry."

"Why aren't more people doing it, then?"

That made him laugh. "Because it's hard, as you're no doubt finding out."

"Anyone can whistle …" she said. Faced with a blank stare from Ward she quickly added, "It reminds me of a song from one of my favorite shows, *Anyone Can Whistle.* It goes … 'I can dance a Tango, I can read Greek—easy. I can slay a dragon any old week—easy. What's hard is simple, what's natural comes hard …'"

Her voice trailed off and she paused, cueing Ward to resume.

He gave her a bemused look and continued. "As managers we're taught that we should invent brilliant processes and then hire capable people to run them. To lead with respect, we're saying that we have to take responsibility for developing the expertise of every employee, and lead him or her to maximize their abilities by designing their own processes. It's quite a radical shift and few managers are willing—or able—to take this step. The fact that it pays back tenfold doesn't make it any easier to do. You've got to learn by practicing."

"And it always starts with senior management. I'm starting to accept that."

"Self-development, then coach others," grinned Ward. "You lead by being on the ground with your staff. You lead by changing yourself, and by taking responsibility to involve others in changing their work, so you can achieve the larger changes you aim for. The small steps of going to see, providing clear direction, and supporting kaizen lead to big changes, not the other way around."

———————

"Finally! My flight is boarding! I'd better dash if I don't want to get stuck at security. One last thing, did you ever solve that slow computer problem?"

"I didn't," she answered with a straight face and grinned when his eyebrows shot up.

"Terry did. Almost by the book, he went through all the possible causes, and the answer surprised us all."

"What did you find out?" he asked.

"Well, we're working with one major bank, and they're crazy about safety systems, which is understandable. As a result, they ask all their contractors to carry the same security system that they do. The bloody thing is massive and regularly updates itself through their central system. It turns out this was slowing our machines considerably at odd times, which is why we couldn't pinpoint it! Now we're isolating the computer relationship with the bank and trying to renegotiate the terms of use of their protection software. Talk about the cobbler's shoes. We're supposed to be the experts and none of us saw it until Terry finally figured it out."

"Good for him. But why did the software get implemented in the first place?"

"Why?" repeated Jane, so taken aback that it made Andy laugh.

"Gotta run," he smiled. "Listen, you're doing good work. You say your results are better, that should be encouraging. This is more like pottery than architecture. You need to keep turning the wheel. Accept that you've only scratched the surface and just keep at it."

"Practice, right?"

"Practice," he waved cheerily as he ran off.

Chapter Five

LEARN TO LEARN

Andrew Ward < andrew.ward@nexplas.com >
To: Jane Delaney < jdelaney@southcape.com >

Dear Jane,

Quick note: I'm attaching the problem-solving format we use.
Everyone in the company should work on one problem at a
time. We also need to discuss the next step of Southcape's
involvement with us.

Best wishes,
Andy Ward

"Come on, Chris, enlighten us," said Mike Wembley jovially.

The difference between genius and stupidity, Chris Williamson's
T-shirt sported boldly, *is that genius has its limits.* The young man was
glancing back and forth from Wembley to Delaney, detouring
intermittently to suss out the problem-solving sheet in his hands. 'Put
yourself in their shoes, look through their eyes,' Jane thought wryly,
imagining being a junior programmer with the CEO and technical
director breathing down your neck. Probably did the little punk good.

"It's a problem-solving sheet," he finally said lamely.

"That's a start," Mike said, with easygoing irony. "The question is:
how is it different from the paperboard? It looks fairly similar. We
thought that since you spend so much time at Nexplas, you might
have some deep insight about how they use this one."

Nexplas problem-solving sheet

Date	Problem	Sketch	Cause	Countermeasure	PDCA Check	Status
						⊕
						⊕
						⊕
						⊕

◐ Problem Identified ◐ Countermeasure Proposed ◑ Countermeasure Agreed ● Problem Solved

"Ah, right, they've got them all over the place. Ward calls the paperboard a confirmation board. This is more of a problem-solving sheet."

"Again, enlighten us?"

Chris stroked his straggly beard, thinking.

"Ward uses the paperboard to give people a hard time about *observation, confirmation,* and *suggestions.* The area manager is supposed to discuss the issues on the confirmation board daily. The team has to write at least one line every day, making sure they agree on the problem description, the cause, and their reaction. It's painful to watch when Ward comes around because he gives them such a hard time about their observation skills: 'Have you seen it for yourself? Does it happen often? Have you noticed anything else? Where, exactly, does the problem appear? Have you confirmed the cause? Have you checked? Do you agree? Have you tried anything else?' He almost always asks them for suggestions, but never agrees or disagrees. Just keeps asking why they think this or that."

"Does he do that often?"

"He's in every other week or so. I only work with procurement, so I wouldn't know what he does with the rest of the company. He doesn't spend more than five or 10 minutes at it. Just breezes in, says hello, and grills them. Oh yes, he always asks them for a shopping list, if there's anything they can think of to make the company work better—barring investment or resources of course," he snickered.

Both directors stared at him.

"Then what about this problem-solving sheet?" Mike asked.

"Well, as I understand it, the paperboard is about learning to react correctly. This sheet is more about reflection. Ward calls it a 'deep thinking sheet,'" he sniggered again.

"Everyone on the team has a problem to solve, kinda like homework. It's not an urgent thing; sometimes the problem has even been solved already. But they're asked to go all the way through to the end of the analysis. They need to confirm what they're doing.

"There's no time pressure on this," he continued. "But they can't start a new problem until they've solved the previous one. The other weird thing is that the bosses often suggest that they work with someone else to solve the problem. It's basic PDCA stuff."

"PDCA, as in Plan Do Check Act," said Delaney, hoping that her confirmation appeared like an explanation to everyone else.

"Yeah. It's a scientific way of looking at the problem. What's your plan? How do you do it? Have you checked the results? How will you act on what you've learned? Ward keeps beating them over the head with it. That's what's written here on the sheet."

"Hmm ..."

"But, to be honest, that's not the most painful tool they have," Chris giggled. "Ward gets them to do this other paperboard sheet. It goes something like this: First they have to write what the problem is from the customer's perspective, then from their own. Next, they draw the ideal process, and spot where they think things are going wrong with the existing process. They measure the defects that occur due to this problem, and nothing else.

"This is hard enough, but where I've seen Ward give them a really hard time is the next bit. He asks them to think of potential factors that could affect the problem and then to confirm them empirically one-by-one. They have to show what experiment they did to confirm whether the factor has a real impact or not.

"It looks like this:

Factor	Impact	Confirmation method	Confirmed (Y/N)
1.			
2.			
3.			
4.			
5.			
6.			
7.			

"You wouldn't believe the grief he gives them over the confirmation method. They're supposed to have confirmed the main factor before they start asking 'why?'"

"Why would he do that?" Jane wondered.

"I was involved in one analysis," he added helpfully. "We were trying to figure out why we had misaligned data from the parts produced in production compared with the parts found in the finished goods inventory. Everyone thought it was an operator problem, since they have to scan every single container that goes onto the pallets and maybe sometimes they plain forget. They were asking 'why would the operator forget' when Ward stopped them and asked them whether the cause was confirmed. It was embarrassing because no one had thought much about it. So he sent them back to observe some more and come back with potential factors.

"They came back with:
   - Operator forgets to flash the container
   - Handheld scanner not available when needed
   - Bad scan from operator or scanner
   - Software mistake

"They asked their team leader to track the discrepancies by double scanning for a few shifts. They found that the biggest issue by far was that the handheld scanner often misfired. So you had to flash the label two or three times—there was no clear indication if the scan had worked properly. The second most frequent factor was that the handheld scanner wasn't available. Turned out they also had to scan the entry of one of the main components which arrived in large containers. This other scanning wasn't that frequent, but still it got mixed up. 'Operator forgetting' came third by a wide margin."

"So asking 'why' wasn't really the point here?" Jane asked. "Sounds like they were barking up the wrong tree?"

"Brilliant!" exclaimed Mike, slapping his forehead theatrically and laughing out loud. "I get it!"

"What?" she snapped—she was certainly not getting anything.

"That's the beauty of the scientific method," he chuckled. "It's counterintuitive. You're not allowed to conclude whatever comes to mind. If we did, we'd still believe the earth is flat—after all it is—and that the sun revolves over it—after all it does. In the scientific method, intuition is only the starting point, but it has no value in itself. What matters is observation and confirmation through experimentation."

They looked at him bewildered. Eventually he would make sense.

"We don't do that. We keep jumping to conclusions and running with the first idea that comes to mind. When that doesn't work out, we try something else, until either the problem has been solved or it has simply gone away."

Jane nodded cautiously. She now remembered that he had been a physics Ph.D. of some sort before drifting into computers.

"But we don't learn much, do we?" he laughed again, still taken up with his 'aha!' moment. "We don't learn because one thing chases another—and it's all pretty much the same anyhow. However, what your chap Ward is doing is forcing his guys to confirm their intuitions. Am I right, Chris?"

"He really takes them to task on it, he does," agreed Chris.

"What happened in the end?" Delaney wondered. "Did they get to the root cause?"

"Nah. In the end, they never did the full exercise because they simply decided to eliminate scanning in the cell. The operator scanned the box of parts when he put it in the cell's stock inventory, and then the tugger driver would rescan it when he picked the box from the cell and placed it on the train. They figured that with their kanbans and frequent pick-ups, they had so few stocks in the cell supermarket that they didn't need the system to know exactly what was on the racks at the production location.

"My problem was that while on the shelf the box was counted in the production system, but once on the tugger it shifted to the logistics systems. So I was dead set against this change to the system. But they thought that eliminating an operator nonvalue-added action was worth the hassle. They also eliminated the handheld scanners and started fixed-post scanning for the kanban cards. This is another topic I'm helping them with now—how to count the kanban cards."

"So Ward was right, in the end."

"He never really contributed much," said Chris, with a doubtful frown. "He certainly never told them to stop scanning. He just kept pushing them on confirming."

"His job is to never share the right answer—the most clever solution." Mike chuckled again, sounding impressed and excited. "He's forcing them to think. He is teaching them not to be satisfied by the first association that comes to mind or by acting on what they remember, but to actually think things through. And look at the results: Why bother improving when you can eliminate. It is brilliant!"

"So we should do it?" Delaney wondered out loud.

"Oh, absolutely, Janey, absolutely," he beamed. "It's going to make us all rich, if we can stay the course. Of course, the developers will all hate it," he added with a laugh.

"Hate it?" she sighed.

"Of course! It's like the testing, don't you see? When you test your code right away, you build in an immediate feedback loop that bites you if you've done it wrong. In practice it means that you can't run away with what you're doing, but have to constantly pay attention. We've found that it orients how people code: they program with the test in mind."

"That's true!" Chris exclaimed. "That's another thing Ward keeps going on about. Every time they want to do something he asks them whether they've got a test method for it. How will they know whether what they're about to do works or not? 'Don't bother to make a proposal if you haven't got a test method,' he keeps saying."

"Exactly, dear boy, exactly. Same thing occurs with the autotests."

"If I read you right," said Delaney puzzled, "we shouldn't expect people to take it upon themselves, then. We'll always have to be on their backs."

"Probably," agreed Mike. "But the rewards should be huge. David would have loved this. Don't you remember, he used to do it with us."

She nodded, thinking back to the late-night sessions with her old boss when they either checked code or sometimes just discussed scenarios or logic. Although he was fond of hearing his own voice, she had learned her trade that way.

"David did it in his own inimitable manner," Mike went on. "But that's exactly what he did, that and the code reviews. He was constantly arguing against the obvious answer, against intuitive common sense. Sure the old bugger was contrarian by nature, but he taught us to think. Now, this problem-solving thing here is a method to do so. We should definitely do this."

"We will certainly need practice," she concluded drily.

"Thank you, Chris," she said as they broke up the meeting. He gave her a geeky grin. "Ward tells me they're still pleased with what you're doing out there."

"That's good to know," Chris mumbled. "But they haven't given me a new assignment for when I'm done finishing what I'm working on."

"You feel it's winding down?" she asked worriedly.

"Hard to tell," he shared. "Their system is still a mess, so there's probably work for years, but they haven't told me what to expect. I know they're having all kinds of discussions—it's all linked to their supplier development program."

"Supplier development program?"

"I don't know much more that," he shrugged. "Do you want me to try to find out more?"

"No, that's all right," she replied. "Just keep on keeping on—make them happy and let me know if you hear something new. I'll ask Ward directly. Thanks again, good job."

Jane cursed as she returned to her desk. No matter how much she tried and how much she talked to Andy, Nexplas remained elusive. Were they being squeezed out of there? Had they done all they could do? They'd just won another bid so staffing was no longer an issue. If anything else, they'd be short of hands soon. But it was still galling.

She consoled herself thinking that, if nothing else it proved that Nexplas operated differently from their other large clients. On the one hand, their VP spent all this effort talking her through the *lead with respect* approach. One the other, their sole contact was a lowly programmer. They had squeezed Sales out of the process completely. She would have to prod Andy on this.

True to his word, Ward had scheduled a check-in of Southcape's efforts with the confirmation paperboards and stopped by the office on his way again from Swindon to Heathrow. Delaney had tried to tell him about their progress, but he told her he would rather see for himself and they could talk it over afterwards.

"This is a good start, but how do you know this is a correct cause statement?" Ward asked a project manager, who was trying to explain a 'project talk' board she'd set up for her team. The woman had never met Ward before. She looked worriedly at Delaney who looked back deadpan, secretly kicking herself—and Ward—for not having a clue of where he was going with this.

"Yes, you're saying here that the problem in the code was an undeclared variable at the IF instruction, right?"

"Yes ..."

"Isn't that the problem, more than the cause?"

"The problem was the bug, surely."

"Well, yes, I guess that my question is what caused the undeclared variable issue?"

"Programmer forgot," the woman shrugged.

"Nope. *Not guilty*, remember?" he said, looking pointedly at Jane.

"Ahrrr ..."

"What caused the programmer to stumble?" he asked. "I'm sure that declaring variables is an important part of your work. So the question is, what happened that made the person skip it? That's the criteria to see if the cause has been properly spelled out."

"Are you saying we should look for the root cause?" asked Jane. "But I thought that ..."

"We're nowhere near the root cause," he interrupted her. "Just a proper expression of the first level of cause. We assume that people want to do a good job. When they don't, we assume that something happened to them to make them do otherwise. That is a *cause*, not a restatement of the problem. Do you see the difference? The question here is: What happened to the programmer that led him to overlook this variable?"

"Well … the generic name of these variables is confusing," suggested the project manager finally, as Ward let the silence linger and showed no sign of moving on. "Unless you have a very clear picture of all variables involved, it would be easy to think this one has been declared …"

"Perfect," he smiled. "That's a cause: the programmer got confused, because the way these variables are named led him to think that it had been declared when it had not. Now we can work on …"

"How we name variables," nodded the woman thoughtfully. "Yes, we often talk about how we should look into our naming schemes, but never quite do."

"Naming variables is part of our core skills," Jane said dismayed, "and we never really look into it? Damn!"

"One thing I meant to ask you," Jane said to Andy as they walked past another project talkboard. "I'm not clear on the difference between these flipcharts—which we're getting the hang of—and the problem-solving sheet you sent us. Mike Wembley, our technical director, got really excited about it, but we don't know quite what to do with it yet."

"It'll come," shrugged Andy. "Look, these paperboards are really about sharpening observation and learning to react quickly. As we walk though, I can glance at them and see that each team looks into at least one problem per day and that all status lines are okay. We're teaching people to see problems, formulate them, and do something about them right away, rather than just work around them."

"Remark and react. I got that. And the other sheet?"

"The paperboard and the sheet operate at two different levels. The board is about learning to spot problems and react quickly. The problem-solving sheet is more of a project manager development tool. It forces the manager to investigate one problem, all the way through a rigorous check, in order to learn the PDCA approach.

"It's not about reaction but reflection. For example, in the case we just saw you might focus on the problems caused by name confusion, ask the project manager to look into this more deeply, and suggest a scheme for better naming variables.

"The immediate problem has been solved, but rather than stop at the first plausible cause she would be expected to look deeper toward the root cause. This all supports *lead with respect*. Ideally, every project leader would:

- Look into one problem a day with his or her team to discuss their observations and reactions.
- Work on one high-level problem in order to learn PDCA.

"The point is not to solve every problem, but to develop a deeper sense of problem solving. This is what we do at Nexplas. But again, this might not be the right way to deploy management by problem solving in Southcape. These are exercises to get you and your people started, but in the end you'll have to figure out which activities work best for your company."

"Speaking of what's best for our company … can I ask your advice on something quite different. I've just lost another experienced programmer," shared Jane, as she ushered Andy in her office.

"Ouch. Good guy?"

"Project leader. Experienced, been with us a good while. I tried to persuade him to stay. Even put a good chunk of money on the table, but he said he didn't like the way the company was going and that what I asked him to do was infantilizing. He didn't want to treat his coworkers like children, or be treated like one."

"Right …," he hesitated. "Is it an isolated case or a hemorrhage?"

"No. There's no brain drain. But he left with a coworker and it's the second case in the past couple of months. Still, I was taken off guard by this one—we had plans for him in the company."

"Hmm. Let me get some context. How are your sales?"

"Good, actually. Maybe even slightly overheating. I keep tracking customer lead-time and we've been making progress. But it looks to be lengthening again, though it's too early to tell for sure."

"And are you keeping up your shop-floor visits?"

"Religiously," she chuckled. "I visit two client sites a week and I have a roster of code reviews, so I get to see every project regularly. And it remains fascinating! I'm learning more than I can process, in fact. I'm also practicing asking 'why?' and letting people make their own decisions—it doesn't come naturally, but I'm working on it."

"Never easy," he agreed. "And?"

"I agree, never easy. But no, that part is going well and I am grateful for all you've taught me. What I'm still struggling with is the T-development angle. It's very constraining and I can feel it creating a lot of resentment in the ranks. I'm at a loss at how to get my people on board."

"Not everyone dreams the same dreams," he answered after thinking it through for a moment. "You've got to respect that, as well. With T-development, we are trying to make our ideal of towering technical expertise a reality …"

"Yes. This was our founder's dream, and I'd like to recapture it."

"But it's not for everybody. Look, a lot of people just want to get on with their job. They don't want to be put on the spot. The dream of excellence is demanding and it doesn't happen just by coasting. Some will be uncomfortable with reaching for it. The core question is how do you satisfy the customers and make a profit?

"In our case, we've formulated a set of ideal goals. May I?" Andy asked, pointing at the large whiteboard on Jane's office wall.

"Please. Go ahead and wipe all that stuff off."

He picked up a marker and began to write. "Right, our ideal state would be:

- 0 accidents, 0 professional illnesses
- 100% quality
- 100% delivery on time
- 100% value-added, 1x1 in-sequence, on-demand
- 100% human development (suggestions from every one)
- 100% long-term partnerships
- 100% of our products renewed every four years

"Clearly, we're not going to achieve this overnight. Some people are uncomfortable seeking something they feel is out of reach. Others don't have the discipline this requires."

"Not everybody dreams the same dreams, I get that," Jane said.

"Here's how we've formulated it," he continued, drawing a two-dimensional chart next to the targets. "There are two essential aspects to development. One is results: achieving objectives. The other is effort: using learning exercises rigorously to think deeply and to get others to think deeply as well.

	Low-improvement effort	High-improvement effort
Achieve objectives	?	**Stars**
Miss objectives	**Problem cases**	?

"Occasionally we're lucky, some people naturally get results and are willing to follow the principles. Nina is one, for instance. Stevey in shipping is another. Luck. Others don't get the results or make the effort. These problems tend to solve themselves sooner or later."

"You fire them?"

"Um. We don't like doing that because if affects mutual trust. Mostly, they leave on their own accord, though sometimes we do have to let them go. In other cases, we just accept that they don't carry their weight and they get what we call a 'desk by the window' far from the action. These are not decisions we rush into. We try to give people time to orient themselves and make their own choices. But the real difficulty is with the other two boxes. People who have results but are unwilling to make the learning and training effort."

"Like the guy I just lost."

"Precisely. Or people who try hard, but somehow don't get the results. At first you tend to encounter the 'cowboys,' the ones that don't cotton to the learning system. Then as these go, you encounter more and more of the second, those who do the homework but learn really slowly. That's even trickier to deal with."

"So I should just let them go, is that what you're saying?"

"No. Not at all. If you think they're good, by all means try to retain them. All I'm saying is don't sweat it if they do leave.

"It's a pain, but you'll see it won't affect the company that much. For instance, our company has become well known because of our results and a few competitors have started poaching some of our middle managers. We were really worried at first, but after a bit the poaching slowed down to a crawl. Word got around that the guys who left for more money weren't any happier in their new jobs—and they weren't as effective as expected outside of our way of working. In the end, it creates headaches, but it hasn't affected us that much."

"You're telling me to cool it, is that it? Just take it calmly."

"Look at it another way. Part of developing people is helping them to succeed in their careers—and a lot of that is up to them, which sometimes means moving elsewhere as a good career move. They may actually be better off elsewhere. Phil and I have quarterly 'people reviews.' We go through the list of my direct reports and we ask: where should this person go next and whom should we move up in their place. For instance, I currently don't have a purchasing manager at the division level; it's all happening at the plant level. This is not necessarily a bad thing, but it means I have to manage the purchasing directors directly, not ideal either. So who?"

"Nina?" she blurted out, realizing immediately she might have overstepped.

"She's a strong candidate," he said carefully, "but I don't know if she's ready or if she'd like it. Would it be good for her career, or setting her up to fail by having to deal with the other plant purchasing directors—who are not a soft bunch, I can tell you. And if she gets the job, who do we move up in her place?"

"What about looking outside?"

"Yes ... but then you take a huge gamble. The people on paper always look better than the people you know—warts and all. But then you have to train them to the way you work and it doesn't often click."

"Considering how differently you look at things, I can see the concern," Jane agreed.

"Indeed ... I personally feel that hiring or promoting people is the single most important decision I can take," Andy continued. "Nobody is irreplaceable and you can always find someone else, but let's face it, it won't be the same team. Because we actually listen to people and make their opinions count, who they are really matters. Once the ship has left the shore, who is on board determines both strategy and operations. With go and see at the gemba we have a pretty good idea of who people are."

"I noticed that. I've found that my opinion of my managers has changed radically since I've started to go and see."

"It does, and it keeps changing. The point is that who they are matters. They have a say on both where you're taking the company and how you're going to get there."

"Exceptional personalities ..." she muttered.

"Huh?"

"Sorry, it's in a paper my daughter got me to read. It says that the most important factor to a business' success are the exceptional personalities of its leaders. The author claims that competitive edge can be explained in terms of:
1. Exceptional personalities
2. Strong leadership
3. Shared common practices
4. Proprietary technologies
5. Reaction to events
6. Culture

"I found it surprising that culture came in so low in the list, but I guess it makes sense," Jane observed.

"Sounds right to me," Andy nodded. "Personalities certainly matter. I find that I look for three things: courage, creativity, and open-mindedness. The courage to face challenges and stick with it even when the going gets tough; the creativity to look at given problems in different ways to invent new options; and the open-mindedness to take other people's new ideas or opinions into account. As for the rest, they could come from another planet for all I care."

"Is that will power and way power?" she mused. "But courage, creativity, and an open mind don't necessarily go together."

"Don't I know it! That's why I'm real careful in hiring and promoting—a bit too much probably. I'd prefer to live with an unfilled position, rather than give the job to someone, and just see how people work together."

"I need to meditate on this," she said thoughtfully. "But in any case, that doesn't help me with the fundamental problem of how I deal with the people I've got now. How do I keep my teams working full speed without becoming a martinet? I'm not even certain how to evaluate and compensate my people anymore. I used to have a clear objective system and now I'm not so sure."

"Objectives are essential," he insisted. "People need to know what to aim for. What we're trying to do is achieve our objectives through developing people. It's very specific. We need to reach our objectives for the company to succeed, but we have to do so by developing our staff. That's an essential aspect of lead with respect: *committing to develop people to the fullest of their abilities*. Without objectives how can they know they're progressing? The harder question is: How do we share our objectives with every employee?"

"Yes, that is exactly what I'm struggling with. I have a better idea of what I want to do with the company, but I don't know how to get it across. Not even with all my directors, actually," she added, thinking of her strained relationship with Rob.

"Guess what?" he chuckled. "We have a practice for this."

"Practice again," she laughed. "Okay. I'm listening."

"Actually, there are three practices:
1. Treat every person as an individual.
2. Practice catchball.
3. Let people know how they're getting along.

"First, we aim to treat every person as an individual. It might sound obvious, but it isn't. We're so convinced that we control systems that we can forget that people are, well, people with their own unique personalities and circumstances.

"In my own case, I'm tied to a horse farm my wife runs in the middle of the French countryside. It was close to the plant I used to manage. I never thought I'd progress beyond site manager without a major life-change, which would've made her miserable. I was surprised when Phil offered me the European job and helped me to define a way to make it work without having to change my other commitments.

"The point is that we have rules and regulations, which are important, but every person is an individual in a unique situation. Practicing respect means making an effort to understand both personality and circumstances."

"Different strokes for different folks, and all that?"

"That's the idea, yes. I'm not saying it's a free-for-all. Procedures need to be understood and respected, obviously. But we'll go out of our way to see each person as an individual and work out issues on a case-by-case basis."

"How can you possibly know every single person that works for you?" she asked, doubtfully.

"Challenging," he admitted. "But go and see helps. Over time, I do get to meet most people on a regular basis. And we have specific systems to help with knowing who people are. Again, practice."

"Second, we practice something we call 'catchball.'"

"Catchball?"

"Yes, bear with me a second. I've come to accept that the degree to which people are engaged with their work is modulated by what I think of as autonomy—the aspiration to be self-directed.

"I was with Nexplas before Phil became CEO. We used to work in a straightforward, pay-for-performance system. To get a bonus, you needed to hit your numbers and that was about it.

"The company was the most political place ever, with everybody playing silly-buggers all the time trying to figure out how to shift the blame and cut corners to hit the numbers—even though it was obvious it didn't work on the shop floor. Nobody cared. Phil came in and he wanted people to be engaged in their work. He wanted them to care. And when they did, the politics improved.

"Sure, money is important. We've got to pay people enough so that money is not an issue. But money isn't the be-all and end-all either. People mostly care about how much money they get compared to their colleagues, so it's a matter of being careful about compensation more than anything else. Once you've taken the money issue off the table, people will care if they feel autonomous in their jobs, they feel they belong to a larger project, and they feel they're improving at what they do."

"Okay ..." she muttered uncertainly.

"Now, as you can imagine, 'self-directed' can be a headache. We most definitely would like people to do what we ask them to and do it in the way we'd like them to. Objectives have to be met and procedures have to be followed. This is an automotive company, not a social club, right?"

"Right."

"This is catchball: I tell my direct reports where I'd like to go. They come up with quantified objectives and a practical plan to get there. And then we wrangle!

"For instance, here's how it worked with Nina. I spent hours with her explaining that I needed radical improvement in supplier performance and getting procurement people to feel responsible for quality and on-time delivery of purchased parts. We discussed it until she could present quantified objectives in terms of supplier bad parts and missed deliveries. I felt she was not being ambitious enough, so we wrangled until we developed stretch goals that we were both okay with, and she put together a plan. We then discussed the plan at length. Essentially, I told her to 'charge the hill' and she came up with the hows and whens. The point is that it's her plan, not mine; her objectives, not mine. But the direction is aligned with the company's.

"Similarly, Len Barton has five clear goals: safety, quality, productivity improvements, flexibility improvements, and a target number of implemented suggestions per employee. The first four are standards for a plant manager in Nexplas, the last one reflects his specific challenge. He set the actual number and wrote the plan on how to get there. Then we wrangled over it for a few hours."

"Is this what your CEO does with you?"

"Uh-huh. He outlines his vision for Europe and where he wants to go, and I come up with a quantified measure of the objectives and a plan. Then we play catchball. For instance, one of this year's goals is to improve supplier relationships across the company—that's one of my key tasks to define and plan. But what I've shown him so far hasn't met his—pretty stretchy, if you ask me—expectations. "

135

"Does your counterpart in the U.S. do the same?"

"Same vision, different way of going about it. We're dealing with a very different customer and supply base—and to be honest, the U.S. VP Mark and I have a very different way of going about things."

"So you're not doing the same thing?" repeated Jane, puzzled.

"Nope. Phil doesn't care about 'same.' He wants us to learn. We discuss our different approaches, which helps us learn from each other. For instance, I'm not big on corporate programs, whereas Mark is more comfortable with that. He started with a supplier conference, ranking best and worse suppliers, and so on—which I haven't done. But based on the success he is achieving, I'll try it next year. I had to accept that I simply didn't see it, so I learned."

"And the CEO just lets you get on with it?"

"He doesn't just let me get on with things. It's the third part of the practice, *he lets me know how I'm getting on*. We agree on objectives and a plan, and then he visits regularly and we discuss. I'm not left alone with my problem. We continuously discuss specifics about his vision and mine, and how well it's going. Confirmation, confirmation, confirmation."

"You're not completely autonomous?"

"Well, I am, pretty much. But I'm not free to do whatever I like if that's what you mean—I'm not *independent*. Autonomy is the ability to solve specific problems in the right way without help. So I'm left alone to make most decisions, but never fully on my own, if you see what I mean. I'm part of a larger project, which is defined by Phil's vision and experience. What's more, I'm quite confident that he's not going to let me do something he really disagrees with without letting me know first."

"Does he let you make your own choices?"

"Sure, all the time. Our ideal is to lead as if we have no power. Sometimes I can tell that Phil doesn't believe I'm going about things the right way. But he lets me experiment and then we discuss what happened. We do the check and act together. I'd never dreamed of that much autonomy in any job. There are so many issues. In fact, I almost feel that Phil leaves me too much scope at times to make decisions, and I get my fingers burnt quite often, believe you me."

"But you're part of a wider project?"

"Precisely. The four of us—the regional VPs in Europe, the U.S., Asia, and Latin America—meet in one of our plants with our staff colleagues every quarter to discuss how we're doing with the vision Phil has outlined for the year. It's fascinating stuff. We deal with different market conditions and different ways of doing things. Not only do we learn, but also we feel that we're creating something together. It's kinda cool really."

"And you do this with all of your direct reports, as well?"

"With all my plant managers, yes. Though I spend more time with the Swindon managers, such as Nina, because it's a new acquisition. I usually go through this exercise with the plant managers and heads of technical center, and they then work with their direct reports. They also meet across functions. For instance, Nina meets with the other procurement heads in each of the European plants every quarter."

"So Nina gets feedback from you on each of your visits and from her counterparts by getting together with them?"

"Yes. She needs to know how she's getting along, and she needs to feel part of a wider project than just her plant. That's the idea. It's my job to give feedback on how she's doing relative to her area and also to other similar areas. It's the way we've set it up in any case."

"Wow. I need to get my head around it!"

"Don't sweat it," he laughed. "At the risk of repeating myself, it's a practice. It's mostly a scheduling puzzle to fit all of these visits and get-togethers within the year. One key strength the company has developed is supercharged personal assistants who can make all these events fit somehow; my assistant Ann is a regular miracle worker."

"So it is completely organized."

"Around calendars, certainly. Again, we're not independent, but we strive for autonomy. I have to work within a precise machinery of learning events. But I am still largely self-directed in defining my objectives and plans, and Phil lets me know how I'm getting along. I try to do this with my direct reports and, more importantly, teach my reports how to do it with their direct reports. That's basically where I always fall down. The Latin American VP is incredibly good at getting her teams to adopt new practices. Me, it takes forever."

"Okay. Let me see if I get this right," Jane said. "I have to practice catchball to engage my employees in defining their objectives and plans according to my vision and ambition for the company."

"Yes. And I haven't got around to doing this with you yet, but that's our next step. For example, how would you suggest you deliver what Nina is looking for?"

She just stared at him ...

"Go and see," she finally picked up, "isn't just about understanding the situation but also about letting people know how they're getting along. I think I see it. But how does it help me with the problem-solving stuff?"

"Give them credit for the work. Praise when praise is due. Most people absolutely crave their boss' approval. Problem solving is a great opportunity to praise them, because as long as they've tried hard enough you can always praise their efforts, whether they succeed or not. Start with JOB = WORK + KAIZEN. As time goes by, the work part gets easier, but the kaizen element remains just as hard as always."

"I'm experiencing this. I hoped it would get better."

"Never does, just accept it. Why should it? Learning is never easy for grown-ups. In order to sustain kaizen, we force people to learn on the job by stopping immediately when things don't go right, and thinking hard about why. This is never going to happen on its own."

"Even though they see the progress?" she asked.

"Oh, they'll enjoy the progress and they will be pleased with it. But they will always find the method hard. Some will accept it more than others. But trust me, when Phil challenges me on something stupid I've done, I still feel bad. I don't worry too much because we've been through so much already, but it's never pleasant. So, we need to accept that stopping at the first defect and writing down the analyses on the various boards is always going to be a pain in the neck."

"Oh, great."

"Which is why we use it to praise people. I rarely tell people they're doing a great job—it's their job after all. But I give them credit for their problem-solving efforts. I congratulate them when they stop a process, rather than continue working when something is wrong. I am respectful of their improvement efforts by recognizing something I think they've done well and letting them know I'm pleased with it."

"If they want your good opinion, they have to do the problem-solving stuff."

"Yes. The more rigorously they carry out the PDCA, the more positive I am."

"Okay. I had completely missed that. Is that why you came to praise Sharon a while ago?"

"Actually," Andy commended, "Sharon had done more than simply solve a problem, she'd proposed a clever innovation. You see, there two types of kaizen:

- *Problem-solving kaizen*: We know what the standard is and we've fallen back, so it's a matter of identifying the gap and finding a remedy to get back to standard;
- *Improvement kaizen*: We're working at standard but seek to be even better by eliminating some form of waste.

"In Sharon's case, she came up with an improvement—something that no one had thought of before that really helped us, which is why I made a point of going out of my way to tell her so."

"Ah, yes ..." she hesitated. "It all sounds so ... calculated."

"It's a method," he laughed. "Do you think that we're born with it? I've been practicing this for years; so much of it has become second nature. And I've got Phil to keep me on the straight and narrow," he chuckled again.

"Practice, yes … aaargh, I'll get it eventually. So one, practice catchball, and two, practice letting people know how they're getting along, and three, practice giving credit for problem-solving efforts."

"That's about it. You'll still have to remind everyone and his dog to be rigorous about PDCA. But these practices do lower the resistance to the formal part of the exercise. Sorry, that's it for now, I have to dash."

"Thanks, this has been incredibly helpful. An eye-opener."

"No worries. And by the way I had a chat with Stevey and Len and they didn't show you the big thing they're doing that I thought you should see!"

"What did I miss?"

"No more today," he grinned, looking at his watch. "Gotta run. You're doing well. We'll discuss it next time you're at the plant."

—————

After walking Ward to his cab, Jane returned to her office and let herself drop in her armchair. Catchball! How would *she* formulate objectives to satisfy Nina Miah's needs? She started doodling on her deskpad and came to the agonizing conclusion that she still did not understand the Nexplas project well enough to formulate clear, quantified objectives that she could get back to Nina with.

The more she practiced go and see, the more depth she saw to the practice—and indeed it was a practice. Once again she concluded, 'the problem is *me*.' How could she steer her project managers if she didn't have a clear idea of what each customer expected from the project? She smiled as she realized for the first time since she started this grueling training program with Ward that 'the problem is me' wasn't scary. After all, this certainly was something she could work on!

She drew a list of Southcape's major projects and then wrote: What do customers want from the project? What are customers trying to optimize in their work? What is the value we seek to provide? …

All good questions, she thought wryly. She realized with a sudden flowering of insight, that in facing problems one after the other and making a greater effort to listen to other people's contributions, she was pushing herself out of her comfort zone, beyond her own pet interests and preoccupations—and truly learning to learn.

As the girls watched a Sunday-evening flick in the living room, Jane worked on her tablet, trying to get her head around the coming week. She kept returning to the same question: how to apply what Andy told her to her team. She wrestled with too many ideas going in too many different directions and found it hard to order her thoughts.

She wrote at the top of the tablet screen:

T-DEVELOPMENT: ACHIEVING OBJECTIVES
THROUGH DEVELOPING PEOPLE

She drew a huge 'T' underneath this, with LEADERSHIP written horizontally and EXPERTISE vertically. Then she considered her project leaders, and realized that for each one of them she had some idea of three problems they could focus on:

- A technical issue to strengthen their IT skills
- A customer issue to stretch their understanding of customer satisfaction
- A managerial issue to develop their relationships with their internal suppliers—the programmers

Her latest conversation with Ward had given her a completely different sense of her work as a manager. She realized how focused she'd been on running the office and kicked herself for not seeing sooner that getting every administrative issue right did not do much for the business. Lead with respect gave her a practical way to manage her firm that she had not seen before.

She wrote JANE DELANEY on top of the T and stared at her name thoughtfully. On the vertical bar, she started listing the practices she'd been learning:
- Go and see
- Follow your customers
- Accelerate the flows
- Show respect
- Grow teamwork
- T-development

To this she added:
- Catchball
- Let people know how they're getting along
- Give credit when due

She'd had her work cut out for her, that was for sure.

With a satisfied smile, she added "Yoga" to the list, glad that she'd somehow found time to take up practicing again. There you had it: more practice. She had resisted the idea at the first, feeling that it was less than rational to go ahead and do something without a clear idea of what the end point would be, to simply trust in learning by doing. But she had to admit it was transforming her and the company.

Then she stared at the horizontal bar: LEADERSHIP. She wrote "stakeholders" and then "???" Rob. Mike. Clients. Bloody Bainbridge.

Bainbridge. She circled the name and sighed deeply. It was time to take the bull by the horns.

Chapter Six

ENCOURAGE INITIATIVE
TO DEVELOP LEADERS

"All right, gentlemen," she said sitting down, looking intently at Mike Wembely and Rob Taylor in turn. "Time to clear the air. I've had a heart-to-heart with our friend Lionel Bainbridge and the private equity partners are very satisfied with our latest forecast. And, *although this has been apparently questioned,*" she said looking at Rob, "they retain full confidence in my leadership. Furthermore, they believe that our quality drive is absolutely the way to go forward. So Mike, we'll continue grappling with test-driven development until it becomes part of the culture. Those who don't like it are free to go."

"What are you saying?" asked Rob angrily. It was hot in the room and Jane could see a sheen of sweat on his heavy face.

"I'm saying, Rob, that I'm drawing the line. No more questioning my leadership to the equity guys behind my back. No more dismissal of Mike's work on testing. We either start working together again—or I'll invoke the separation clause in the shareholders' agreement."

"You can't do that," he said, blanching.

"Try me. I've cleared it with Bainbridge. No one wants it, but he said, and I quote: 'You're the CEO. You do what you have to.'"

Mike broke the ensuing silence with a chuckle. "Oh, come on children. Enough with the testosterone, what? Janey darling, why don't you tell us what you have in mind?"

Silently blessing Mike's eccentric heart, Jane nodded and continued. "I've been visiting all our clients regularly—which I know you don't like, Rob, but you'd better get used to. And I've learned a few important things.

"First, we are not spending enough time upfront to understand what our customers really value; what it is they're trying to optimize, not what we can provide. And two, we don't need a sales team to sell a white elephant, customers ask for these on their own. What we need is a sales team that will sell the kind of work we can make good margins on, work that is recurring and core business."

"But ..." spluttered Rob.

"I'm not done," she cut in rapidly. "I've also been tracking our delivery lead-time and realized that we go through cycles of feast and famine. If there's too much activity, we stop selling in earnest because we know we can't deliver. Then when this starves the pipeline, we switch to full-on sales mode and bring in contracts we don't know how to make money on. This is the main problem I want us to work on."

Rob remained silent. Mike was nodding approvingly.

"I don't know how we're going to achieve this, but the three of us will meet once a fortnight to discuss this issue. This meeting will be mandatory," she announced, looking straight at Rob.

"The agenda for the next meeting, which I've already asked Alyson to schedule in your calendars, will be to review your proposals to make this work. I'm seeking a way to level our order intake. I expect you two to work together to come up with a quantified objective and a practical implementation plan. That will be all, gentlemen."

"Is this how it's going to be from now on? Toe the line or else?" spluttered a livid Rob.

She didn't answer but stared back, resolute.

"Come on, you two, come on," scolded Mike, standing up. "Janey, you've made your point, no need to rub it in. Come on, Rob, I'll buy you a drink. We need to chat."

———

"Er ... one last thing," Bainbridge said, sipping his coffee, setting off Jane's warning alarms.

She was already wary. She'd been taken aback when he unexpectedly invited her for lunch at his club, a well-known celebrity watering hole and a shrine to customs so old-fashioned that she was surprised that females were even allowed in.

She assumed that he invited her to announce that the equity partners had decided to sell Southcape. When they put the deal together to purchase the firm from David, Bainbridge said they generally re-sold the businesses they invested in every three to four years, so she'd been waiting for them to put the firm on the market.

Not so. In the light of rather unfavorable market conditions, he said that Southcape was one of the firms they were keeping. They believed they could make a much larger profit selling it later on.

She waited patiently for him to reveal the real agenda. He was an older gentleman with an inscrutable face and foppish mannerisms—there was a story there, she thought wryly. Even though he had been nothing but supportive of her over the last few months, she still found it difficult to like or trust the man.

"We've ... well ... there is a new opportunity. Another software company has been brought to our attention; about the same size as your outfit. It's in a bit of a mess, so the price is very attractive. A fire sale, one could say.

"We'd be interested but we don't want to ... how do I put it ... extend our portfolio at this stage. We wondered whether Southcape would be willing to make the acquisition. We'd arrange the financial backing, of course."

She stared at him, at a loss for words. *No!* She screamed inwardly. We're not ready, no way, it's too much, we can't ...

"Delighted!" she heard herself say with as much enthusiasm as she could muster. "We'd be absolutely delighted."

"Splendid," Bainbridge smiled. "You're taking a load off my chest. We'd be doubling the value of our investment," he added with a rapacious glint in his eye. "And we're confident you're the right person to turn it around."

———

"That concludes our business then," said Nina Miah at their next meeting at Nexplas. "I'll be expecting a proposal from your office."

Jane smiled, hiding her disappointment that Nexplas still wouldn't consider a full system overhaul. But they had agreed to keep on a team of three people to continue to improve the IT systems. That would be Chris, Sharon (they thought the world of her), and whomever else she could staff.

"By the way," Nina said as they went down the stairs, "Andy said he wanted to have a word before you left. He's in production. I'll find you some safety gear and walk you over."

———

They found Ward leaning against a wall next to a coffee machine in a production rest area, listening intently to a debate between Len Barton and another bullet-headed gent she hadn't met before. Did they all share the same barber?

Voices were low and brows were furrowed. Ward motioned her over without a word and exchanged a quick wave with Nina, who excused herself with a smile and a nod and returned to her work.

"You know what she's like, Len. Be fair!" said the man whom Jane didn't know.

"Sure I know, but the fact is that her foot is bandaged, so telling her just to lace up her shoe isn't going to help much, innit?"

"She never said nothing!"

"Gentlemen, let's not lose the point," intervened Ward.

"The pedal she's using is hard," he observed, "and whether she's hurt herself at home or here is beside the point. If she says it's the machine, we count it as an accident. End of story. Second, we obviously need to kaizen this operation. Agreed?"

He ended his talk by walking over to join Jane, letting the two men sort things out between themselves.

"Trouble?" she asked when they were out of earshot.

"The usual," he answered with a tight smile. "We were looking at the cell when Len noticed the operator had her shoelace undone. He told the supervisor, who immediately went to tell the woman off. The operator explained that she had hurt her foot and had to wrap it, so she couldn't tie her shoe properly. Fact is fact, she has a repetitive operation involving a foot pedal that is well within safety regulations, but could still be the source of her injury. The main issue, however, is that this is one of the old-style supervisors we simply can't seem to turn around."

He sighed, shaking his head. "The good thing, I guess," he said after a while, "is that Len did see the problem and is addressing it."

"What did I miss here?" wondered Jane, as they got to Stevey's assembly area.

The short supervisor was in a cell, looking at a piece of equipment with one of the operators. He walked over when he saw the two of them approach.

"Hi, Stevey. Would you show Ms. Delaney your dojo?"

"What?" She'd heard 'mojo' which didn't add up, she thought, amused.

"Dojo," repeated Andy. "It's a Japanese term for training hall, a place to practice. To learn by repeating set movements until the body knows them intuitively."

"Ah. More Japanese."

"We're not too bad," he sighed. "We try to avoid using too much lean vocab, but we feel that *gemba*, *kaizen*, and *dojo* have enough specific meaning that we use the original word. That's about the only Japanese terms we do use, come to think about it."

"I've got me own dojo, a minitraining center, so to speak," Stevey explained, pointing to a couple of workstations surrounded with panels covered with paperboard sheets and design photos.

"But beggin' your pardon, Mr. Ward, if you want the full story, it didn't start like that. Mr. Ward here fair changed what used to be my job first. Used to be an effing nightmare, if you'll excuse my French. I used to spend my day running after missing parts, running after bloody maintenance to keep the machines going, moving people around to follow the computer's orders. Hated the bloody thing. It was running me ragged.

"Then Mr. Ward took me to a cell and said, 'Stevey, mate, the customer uses one of these parts per engine, and builds an engine every minute, so forget the computer. Your job is to come up with one part a minute, and follow these kanban cards we're putting in place.'

"That 'one part every minute' changed everything. It helped us to see all the problems we had to keep to that pace. Not only did we have issues with this or that, but I realized that if I had to come up with one part a minute, every operator should do a job in the minute, which wasn't the case by a long mile, no ma'am.

"So we had one of them kaizen workshops Mr. Ward kept hassling us about, and we started solving some big ergonomics issues I'd never bothered with. We balanced the work, and then there we were with needin' four people instead of six on the line.

"So Mr. Ward says, 'Stevey, pick your two best operators on the cell, and we'll ask one to do the same job on the next cell, and the other will stay here and work as a team leader—he makes parts some of the time, and the rest he makes sure we can stick to *exactly* one part a minute.'

"Now, that sounded weird, but we done it, and it worked! Except that now we see that we have so many quality problems and all. And I don't understand why some shifts simply have more rework and scrap than others. Mr. Ward says, 'People are all different, so maybe they don't work the same way. So here's what you're going to do. Every day, Stevey, you're going to spend half an hour training an operator. You, personally.'

"'Training to do what?' I ask. 'An operation', he says. So we set up this board here," Stevey continued, taking them to yet another large whiteboard on the side of the cell. Across the top it read:

TRAINING PLAN
SUPERVISORS TRAIN ONE OPERATOR PER DAY EVERY DAY

"Y'see, every operator that works in this cell has a session planned with me for training. Since I run 37 people, I don't see them that often, but they know they're all going to be trained. Whether they're old timers or young'uns, makes no difference. Everyone has a session with Stevey. I do this across the area, so I'm back in the cell every four or five weeks for the training."

"What do you train them at?" wondered Jane, intrigued.

"That's exactly what I asks," he chuckled. "'Making parts,' Mr. Ward answers. He says, 'open a folder,' and he gives me this:

Step	Operation	Point to watch out for	Idea for waste elimination

"We've got all these operations procedures an' so on, but he says start with this. So I do. Now two things happen. First, although we all know how to do the job, I realize that on some detailed operations, every one's got their own way of doing things. And second, operators have all sorts of ideas about how to do the job better, but no one's ever asked them.

"So Mr. Ward, who's not one to leave things alone—if I may say so—says 'Stevey mate, you've got to put another board up:'

Status board

New suggestion	Confirmation (find a place to test)	Validation (get others to agree)	Standardization (include in standards)

"We'd had suggestion programs of every kind before so I don't want to do it, because we always get all kinds of silly ideas. But he says it's not a program. It's just for me. So we try it. And I have to give it to them, people give me fair ideas, they do."

"Engagement?" she asked, looking at Ward.

"Asking the right questions," Andy confirmed. "By looking at detailed operations, people understand the questions we're asking, so they have good ideas. It's always back to stand in their shoes, look through their eyes. If we manage to get into their world of producing parts every hour, we discover a gold mine of ideas."

"Fair surprising it was. Then I ask Mr. Ward, 'If there's a right way to do some of the difficult operations, why don't every one apply it?' He says go ahead—calls them standards. 'Write them up and train people to apply them,' he says. 'But don't do it for them. If they won't do it, there's a problem.'"

"Standards?" Jane asked.

"Yes, standards." Andy paused.

"It's a tricky subject," he continued. "Let me backtrack. Standards have a specific meaning in this context for us. you see, a large part of being respectful is that we organize work around human motion, no matter how large the machinery, the person remains in charge. They are not a slave to the robot, they make the parts *using* the robot.

"It's the same with IT in fact—the person does the work and the system helps, not the other way around. This is one of the basic reasons that lean differs from Taylorism: every team member is an essential worker no matter how complex the equipment they use—they are not a human part in an automated system.

"The question is how to coordinate people, machines, and facilities to produce the most value and generate the least waste. To work efficiently, we must agree on the best work sequence that generates the least waste. That's our definition of a standard: the best sequence of steps that describes how we should work now. Standard here means reference, not rule. Standards are to be followed, but most importantly, they are to be improved."

Ward paused for emphasis, then continued: "They're not standard operating procedures and they're not written in stone. They're the result of collective observation and improvement, so that we know that they are the best current way to work. And they are the basis for improvement; they're the very starting point of kaizen."

"In fact," he said, warming unexpectedly to this theme, "it's a question of respect—again. There is nothing worse for an operator than to feel they're doing their best, but that their boss is never happy about the quality of their work."

"We've all been there," Jane agreed.

"We work to give people confidence that they're doing a good job, so that they can work with peace-of-mind. People want to make good parts, and not be caught out making bad parts—particularly if they didn't know that it was a bad part. Even worse if the bad part is caught on the customer line, because then all hell breaks loose.

"It's our job to teach people to distinguish *okay* work from *not okay*. For each job we need to clarify:
1. Targets in terms of customer expectations
2. Step-by-step breakdown of the job
3. Necessary conditions to do the work right
4. Clear 'OK' vs. 'Not OK' judgment criteria"

"That's what really clicked for me," the older man confirmed. "When Mr. Ward asked me to train a person a day, I thought he was daft. I could see no problem with the newbies, but I really couldn't see myself going to teach some guys who've been here as long as I have how to do their job. But when we started going into the details of what is *okay* or *not okay* every one just opened up and we realized we had different notions all around.

"Mr. Ward talked to us about them 'boundary conditions' where things are really unclear. So we worked with his documents and broke down every job into individual elements, and then tried to friggin agree on *okay* versus *not okay* for every task—and I have to include safety. So we review step-by-step what needs to happen to make an okay part safely, and what the specific tasks are to watch out for in terms of safety and quality. We've been doing this for more than a year, and we're still finding out things.

"Which is how we started this dojo. After several months, I'd come to the conclusion that there were only a few difficult operations in every cell. Some are technically difficult because the machine has not been designed right, some require skills such as manual de-burring, and some are plain repetitive such as carrying a part. So this is what we do in this area here. Team leaders and more experienced operators train others on these few actions.

"I didn't believe in it at first, but it's made such a difference to both quality and productivity—particularly with the young'uns and the temps."

"Do a few things very well," said Jane with sudden insight. "Do operators really write standards?" she asked, to make sure of what she was hearing.

"It depends on what you mean," Andy hedged. "To start with, manufacturing engineering writes the process to make the part: what steps in what order. But they stop there. When it comes down to the actual movement—feet, hands, eyes, that sort of thing—then it's the operators experience that matters."

"So operators write their own rules about how to handle parts."

"They're not rules," he corrected. "They're standards—the best current known way to make the part with the least waste. I'd like to say, the ideal way, except there is always some waste to spot and eliminate. Standards change as people learn how to work better and as the line changes in volume, in mix, starts new products, or through kaizen. But yes, the supervisor writes standards with the teams. The role of the team leaders is to know these standards like the back of their hands, and to make sure operators know them as well."

"Apply them you mean?"

"Well ... mostly, yes. But again, it depends. A left-handed person won't hold parts or equipment like a right-handed one, or a short person like a tall one, and so on. So we pay attention to individual specifics. The standard is the best-known way to work right now, but we respect the fact that people may have valid reasons to do it differently."

"The point is to have that conversation," Stevey added. "Then they either change their minds or we learn more about the standard. It's what makes the job interesting, really."

"Are you ready with your stuff, Stevey?" Ward asked the supervisor. "We'll have to get a move on if we don't want not to rush for the plane for a change."

"I'm ready. I'll just go get my bag."

"Are you going to the airport?" Jane asked.

"Yes, we're going to the German plant, where Stevey is going to help them out with setting up their own dojo."

"Do you want me to drive you there, since I'm going that way anyway? There's something I'd really need your advice on."

"That would be great, thanks."

"By the way," Andy continued, "back to your point about doing a few things very well. The real difficulty is to know which things we need to do really really well in the whole scope of what we have to do every day. In this respect Stevey's done well. You'd also find a dojo in Tim's area in logistics. Ideally, each supervisor would have one—but I'm far, far from that."

"Do they still continue the half-hour training per day?"

"Of course. It's not just about making parts; it's the relationship as well. They get to spend half an hour working closely on operations with one operator per day. It's amazing what comes out of it. This is also where they hear all sorts of personal concerns, which they can address on the spot rather than let them fester."

"I wonder how it would play out at home," Jane thought aloud. "It's not impossible—the agile gang speak of peer programming with tears in their eyes. I guess I could ask each division leader to spend 20 minutes a day looking at the code with his guys."

"It wouldn't be just the code but how they create it, how they go about it, etc. Just do it," Ward suggested, "and see how it goes. It's not quantum physics—it simply needs doing."

"Wait. Hang on a second." Ward had spotted something at the assembly cell. "What's that?" he asked, pointing toward a small grimy plastic container separated into two compartments by a piece of cardboard. The operator had just thrown something in it and the movement had caught his eye.

"We were discussing this when you came up earlier," said Stevey, who had returned with his suitcase. "Not sure whether it's a proper suggestion or not. Madison Abbot is the team leader here. Let me call her over. Maddy? Hi, luv, would you come here a sec?"

The team leader came to join them from the cell where she had been manning a station, and Stevey made the introductions.

"I'm sorry, sir," she said to Ward, "but I can't stay long, we're one short today."

"No problem," he smiled back. "Just a quick question: that plastic container with the inserts in it? Someone's idea?"

"Lacey came up with it, but she's at home with flu today. We get so many problems with these inserts when the machine assembles them. She thought she could visually inspect the ones the machine rejected. Then we noticed that some are definitely not right—she chucks them in the left side of the bin—and that some are fine but with too much grease on them—she puts them on the right."

"Looks like most have too much grease," observed Ward.

"Aye. At first we thought we were having so much trouble because the parts were bad, but the machine also rejects them when the grease is too thick. I've been looking at the greasing process, but don't know what to do about it."

"Why do we grease these?" asked Ward.

"I've asked the engineering lads about it, but you know that lot," Stevey huffed. "They haven't got back to me yet."

"Well, that definitely counts as a suggestion," Ward concluded.

"But it doesn't improve the process as such," the team leader Maddy observed.

"It helps us understand it better. So it's definitely a smart idea. Congratulate the lady when she's back, will you? And Stevey, we also need to check with purchasing , how come operators have to deal with faulty inserts?

"Good job every one, ta."

"Can we come back to suggestions?" Jane asked, as she sped onto the M40.

"Huh?" Ward stirred. "Sure. Let's start with the premise that we *want* suggestions, right? Our goal is that each person contributes to the business and each person should feel they've contributed. We do ask that suggestions never cost very much, if anything. We also ask people to be aware of how the suggestion reveals a better way of thinking about something. Let's also keep in mind that if we reject a suggestion, the employee is not likely to submit one again right away. So we want *implementable* suggestions, and the employees should be able to participate in the implementation themselves. It's our basic premise. Okay with that?"

"Okay so far—you want suggestions, not for their economic benefit but for engagement. I'm with you."

"Engagement and involvement. Phil's got an equation for this:

JOB SATISFACTION = ENGAGEMENT + INVOLVEMENT + RECOGNITION

"We want people's brains on the job, but remember that we also want them to feel part of something bigger, to contribute to the cell, the site, ultimately the company. So if the employee does not implement personally, we lose a large part of the benefit."

"Hmm—they'll be proud of something they did themselves," Jane offered.

"Right. So if we want suggestions, we're going to have to work at getting implementable ones, and that's an important part of the supervisor's job. For example, when that woman who's out today ..."

"Lacey," said Stevey.

"Thank you, when Lacey has the notion of examining why a component is wrong, it's Maddy's job to help her clarify her idea by using simple form we have for suggestions. They go together to the gemba and—"

"Observe and discuss," Jane threw in.

"Observe and discuss, absolutely. The employee explains in detail what the problem is, how it affects them, and the impact on the work. The role of the team leader is to listen and clarify."

"That would be, 'engage in solving problems and demonstrate that opinions count.'"

"Precisely. As it happens, it's not easy. The problem is usually clear for the employee, but not necessarily well expressed. The team leader needs patience to explain that a clear formulation is important to get other team members on board with the suggestion. It's usually a matter of a few minutes, but this is a critical part of the suggestion process. We've got a form that I'll send you, where the team leader and employee draw:

- Before (with visible waste)
- After (improvement idea)
- Benefit (expected and costs)

"Once the employee has completed the form, she places it on the board we saw, and the supervisor makes sure the suggestion moves forward. This board is the supervisor's—in this instance, Stevey's—and it's his tool to track his own suggestion process. The form goes into the 'new' box, and then the supervisor has to find a cheap and practical way to test the idea with the employee. In most cases, this is not a problem as most suggestions are very down to earth, but in a few instances there are one or two points to check, such as quality or manufacturing engineering. The supervisor has to make sure they're not touching something else, which might cause an unwanted side effect. Again, this shouldn't take weeks. It's a matter of asking the right question to the right person."

"We do try to give a quick answer," Stevey chipped in, " but that's easier said than done. It's not that we're lazy or slow to respond. We try to move the form to the next step in under a week and get it accepted by the other members of the team. But pretty often the suggestion hits a snag and something further needs to be checked."

"Often when there's some small investment involved," Andy agreed. "We don't like suggestions needing investment—but we don't want to lose the ideas either. Or there are some particularly rigid quality procedures on the line contractually negotiated with the customer, things like that. This can take a while. But again, this should be a pretty rare occurrence.

"Two things are happening with the overly greasy parts," he continued. "First, the operator, is engaged in her work—she is interested in why the inserts are being rejected by the assembly machine, she is helping to improve the process, she brings the plastic container to the cell, and tries out her idea. It might not look like much, but she's taking initiative with the support of her team leader.

"The second thing that is happening through the approval process is that Maddy and Stevey, the team leader and the supervisor respectively, have to work together to root out the causes of the problem the suggestion addresses and evaluate how sensible the countermeasure is. Each suggestion is an important opportunity for engagement on the operator side, and teamwork for the rest of the organization."

"Do you ever reject suggestions?"

"Sure we do, but we try not to. Rejecting a suggestion sends the wrong message. Of course it happens. But bear in mind that our suggestion process is as much a training system for supervisors and team leaders to engage their employees in solving problems and contributing to their workplace, as it is for getting operators to make suggestions. As you can imagine, our major headaches are with the supervisors' training more than employee's ideas. When a supervisor hasn't been able to properly sort a suggestion in its early stages, sometimes they just have to reject it.

"And sometimes workers will make suggestions simply to make a point: they'll come up with something they know we won't accept just to show us they disagree with something or other we have done. In other cases, the suggestion really goes against some policy—mostly quality in automotive—or some technical difficulty the supervisor hasn't seen outright, and then it has to be rejected. The key here is to explain clearly to the person why the suggestion cannot be adopted."

"You don't follow their suggestion, but it still matters."

"That's the basic principle. Our aim is 90% approval, but as you know, life at the gemba is rarely that simple. Still, we have a few team leaders who are really skilled in the process and succeed in getting suggestions out of all their employees *and* who work well with their supervisors, so that together they keep the rejection rate below 5%. They're usually the more experienced leaders, who are both technically skilled and have a good relationship with their teams."

"Right, so that's how you get such a high approval rate," she said, sounding impressed.

"Yeah. However, approval is only the beginning. Remember we're aiming to create a sense of *pride* among employees, which is created when they have fully contributed to designing and improving their own work."

"So that's why they need to implement themselves, is that it?"

"That's the idea," agreed Stevey.

"Our next step is *confirmation*," continued Andy. "Right, Stevey?"

"Yes, sir."

"Confirmation?" Jane asked, surprised. "But I thought the supervisor has already approved it?"

"That's just approval. Confirmation means that we know the suggestion can work in practice. So the supervisor will find some time for the operators to experiment with their suggestion. Together they'll try it out by jury-rigging something, somehow. I don't know if you've noticed, but in the factory we've got quite a few devices which are just cobbled together with cardboard and tape, that sort of thing."

"I did notice it, actually. That plastic container didn't look like much of anything," she noted.

"Yeah, I know, we experiment with bits and bobs. 'Use your head, not your money' kind of thing. The point is, we try suggestions out before building them in hardware. The team leader has a key role—they coach the operator to find a clever, simple way of testing an idea.

"The important thing is that they're working together on this, on the floor, thinking with their hands. What we're fundamentally aiming for is involvement and teamwork. We want the operators to have ideas and participate. We want team leaders to work with their supervisors and operators, to involve them in having a say on how things run. It's a collaborative effort."

"And not bloody easy," muttered Stevey.

"When do you consider the suggestion implemented, then?"

"Hang on, we're not done yet,'" laughed Andy. "Once they've found a simple way to test the idea, they need to convince all the other team members that it is a real improvement, and not just some crackpot scheme."

"Shared success again?"

"And pride. Pride because their colleagues recognize that they came up with a good idea that helped the team as a whole. So the team leader arranges time to discuss the experiment and get other people to weigh in and maybe contribute further. This is not always easy, either. With less experienced supervisors and team leaders, it can be a tricky moment."

"When the teams have approved the idea, then the supervisor and team leader come up with a plan to get the suggestion properly implemented. At this stage, chances are some maintenance or engineering time will be required and this needs to be scheduled. When they actually build the device, or change the cell, or adjust a machine, etc., the operator is present and contributes.

"For instance, I'm sure you've seen that we use a lot of flexible tubes to build installations around machines to handle parts, packaging, and tools. The great thing about this is that with very little training, operators can actually build stuff for the line, and change it later on as they come up with further improvements."

"Wow!" Jane exclaimed after a while. "That seems like a lot of work for each suggestion."

"No joke, ma'am," chortled the supervisor.

"The interaction is the point," explained Andy. "The interaction each suggestion fosters is part of the engagement process. It really depends what you look for in suggestions. It's not that much work to make our employees feel proud of themselves and to train our supervisors to deepen their managerial skills. The truth is, the amount of work really depends on the supervisor's proficiency. Those who are good at this handle the process quickly and seamlessly. Suggestions keep flowing in their areas and not surprisingly, productivity is high and absenteeism is low. Others are more problematic. We train and train, but it's never easy.

"However, I have to stress how important this is to us, and we enjoy massive benefits even when we're not great at it. It's clearly not the easiest thing we do, but it's a key goal for the plant manager. Suggestions are a definite, concrete topic where we can truly *lead with respect*—all the way to operator engagement and involvement, so it's well worth the effort."

———————

"You said you wanted to discuss something," Andy asked, as they hit the traffic around Heathrow Airport.

"Yes!" Jane replied, trying to gather her thoughts. "There's just so much stuff to learn. Dojo. Suggestions. Confirmation. It seems very powerful, but ah …"

"Rome wasn't built in a day. Remember, this is the third or fourth time I've done this from scratch, so I've gained experience. It's easier when you know where you're going. The one thing to keep in mind at this stage is to give your employees confidence in their *okay* versus *not okay* judgment."

"Yes. That's all good. But actually, I wanted to get your thoughts on something completely different, relating to Southcape." She outlined her conversation with Bainbridge and the unfolding due diligence. "So it looks like we're going to buy them, and double in size almost overnight …"

"And you don't feel ready for it."

She nodded slowly.

"I feel your pain," he laughed quietly. "I was barely getting my head out of the water with my first plant when Phil gave me two other plants to run—and an engineering division. I survived, barely, and then he gives me the European division. Then he goes off and buys more plants. We're never ready. We grow or we grow old."

"Sure …," Jane considered, "but as you just explained, managing the way you do demands a lot of personal attention to people. You need to teach them to make things visual and then look out for problems. Then you jump in and get them to tackle their own issues, which requires following up, and so on and so forth. How do you deal with rapid increases in footprint?"

After a long silence he replied, "The job of leaders is to develop more leaders. The nub of your—our—problem is that you can only grow sustainably as fast as you develop leaders to support growth.

"I don't say this to critique your driving, but speed can in fact be harmful. And I'm not just talking about leadership roles, but leadership in general. For any leader to be effective in an executive position, he or she needs to have developed leaders amongst all employees. You have to create a leadership network. People others look to, who will convince the crowd to follow your lead. Not everyone is expected to be a leader, of course. In our case, several team leaders and operators are real leaders: They are well liked and respected by the other operators, and their opinions and reactions count highly to move people one way or the other."

"I can think of a few," chuckled Stevey. "Not necessarily the loudest mouths either."

"Develop leaders? I thought leaders were born, not made," Jane said archly.

"Not in our experience," shrugged Andy. "We're not looking for great leaders from history books. We're looking for people with solid judgment who can influence others in dealing with the changes that will inevitably affect us all. Leading change to adapt is what it all comes down to, and no one leader can do this on their own. They need others to support them."

"But how can you possibly do that?"

"We *manage for change* by training people to solve problems daily and by changing how they do things in a day-to-day, low-fuss fashion."

"Manage for change?"

"Sure. Some of these practices should be familiar to you. We try to organize them in ways that connect the practice or tool to the larger principle. In order to manage for change, every manager in the company is taught to:

1. Make activities or processes visible to reveal problems.
2. Stop and react to protect the customer.
3. Solve problems one-by-one.
4. Check and let people know how they're getting on.
5. Improve processes accordingly (at senior level, policies).

"That's actually all I do, day in, day out. In practice, managing for change means that I make sure training to standards is happening and I keep kaizen moving by stepping in when I see a problem. I look at how problems are revealed daily, I give problem-solving exercises to people, and follow them up."

"It sounds hard to believe that's all there is to it," she protested.

"It's learning by doing," he grinned. "For instance, we just had a fairly successful start of production with our new German product, which is where we're going now.

"It's a huge relief, because this is a high-stakes project. Most of the engineering issues I had to deal with went way over my head. My role was essentially to spend time with the guys, get them to listen to each other, push them to formulate their problems better, and know when to look for expert advice outside the group. I even learned a few new engineering tricks in the process."

"Sounds fascinating," she replied.

"Over the years," he continued, "you discover that there are *typical problems* and *typical countermeasures*. So yes, it gets easier. In many cases, I have no clue how to solve the problem, but I have a pretty good idea of how to get into it, what analysis method is likely to work, and so on. By solving problems on a daily basis, you learn to deal with unexpected situations as part of the job. Change is no longer a big one-off thing—it happens routinely, every day. And when you've done the groundwork of engaging and involving people, they keep surprising you as well. Don't they now, Stevey?"

"That they do!"

"The funny part that took me years to learn," Andy reflected, "is that standards are the key to managing for change."

"How's that?" she asked. "It sounds like a contradiction in terms. Aren't standards supposed to stabilize things?"

"Tell me about it. But yeah, the change I'm talking about is not big random change. It's about following our customers. This is very specific change: we need to change our production more often to be more flexible and follow customer demand. We need to introduce new products more often to follow customer tastes. We need to make improvements more often to reduce waste and follow our customers' prices and still make a profit. It's that kind of change.

"So of course standards help, without standards all of this is much harder. Standards are the key to training ourselves to change. Daily problem solving prepares people to face the unexpected. Standards give them the confidence to switch from situation A to situation B without feeling overwhelmed. Kaizen and standards are two sides of the same coin. The palm and the back of the hand, if you will."

"Managing for change and organizing for learning. Well that certainly gives me a lot to think about!" she exclaimed.

"Now, here we are," she said, exiting the motorway. "Which terminal are you flying from?"

"Hey, we were lucky with the traffic, looks like we're early for once," Ward observed. "We've got at least an extra hour before we need to check in. Why don't we swing by your offices and see where you've got to?"

"Ah … sure," she answered taken aback and suddenly wondering what they'd find walking in at the end of the day without warning. Oh well, she sighed to herself. She'd learn something in any case.

———

There was a stand-up meeting in progress as they entered the project room. Everyone was very quiet. Jane first thought they'd fallen silent because the three of them had entered the room, but now looking at the tense faces she wondered what they'd stepped into.

"Hello, everybody," she said chirpily. "You all know Andy Ward and this is Stevey … ahh …"

"Davies," the Nexplas supervisor finished nodding pleasantly.

"Hi, every one," Andy waved. "Please carry on, we're just observing, as always. Oh, hi, Sharon."

Sharon Miller mumbled something, looking hesitant. Jane thought she looked upset—was it Ward? Still, the meeting didn't pick up and the silence grew increasingly heavy.

"We call this a stand-up meeting," Delaney finally explained. "Every evening the project teams get together and they establish what needs to be done to make tomorrow work. We make a daily list on this whiteboard, so we can track what issues get solved and which don't.

"Come on, people," she finally challenged the team after more awkward silence. "Out with it."

"Um," the project leader hesitated—it was the same stout woman Ward had discussed 'project talkboards' with but couldn't remember her name. "We're having difficulties with the customer on this one—you know what bankers can be like. We're trying to define the problem better upfront, but they won't let us talk to the final users in the back office."

"Why?" Jane asked, puzzled.

"They worry that we'll ask questions that will upset them. They seem to have some sort of issue about this. I believe that we can continue scoping the project and sort this out later, but not everyone is in agreement."

Jane looked around at the project team, but no one spoke up.

"Well?" she asked.

"I don't believe we can scope the project without first clarifying the user interfaces by talking with the actual users," Sharon blurted out.

"Cindy?"

The project leader paused before answering, appearing a bit piqued over Sharon's comment. "I can see Sharon's point, and technically she is correct, as the user interface is an important part of this work … but in this case, I feel we need to listen to our customer, accept their desire that we not talk with the users, and find a way to work around the issue."

"Ha!" snorted Stevey unexpectedly.

All eyes turned to the small graying gentleman whose smile bordered on mocking. Delaney glanced at Ward, who had retreated to his favorite hideaway of lounging against a wall. What now?

"We get this all the time," the Nexplas supervisor exclaimed. "Innit right, Mr. Ward?"

Ward made an "it's your show" gesture and kept his peace.

"What does your company really value?" Stevey asked them.

They stared back, not knowing how to answer.

"On the one hand, you want to do the job right, and on the other management tells you not to rock the boat, that it?" he chuckled in his

166

all-knowing way. "You have to ask yourself, what is your number one value? And are you being consistent with it? I make a few parts for Toyota, not a very high runner. Couple of weeks ago, I get a call from my boss because a team leader from Toyota has shown up at reception without warning with a defective part in hand.

"They had traced the part to my area, so I went to talk to the chap. He didn't want to talk to me; he wanted to speak with the operators in the cell making the part. So I takes him to the shop, and he shows a side of the part we deburr because we can't get it out of the machine right first time.

"This part is okay, he explains, but it's borderline; some are fine and some are not. This means that they have to continually check these parts in detail before assembly. First of all, they don't want to make defective cars and second, vigilance on these parts is overburdening the operator assembling that module, who has enough to do without worrying about our part. Then he goes on and describes exactly what the issue is with the part and what we should be careful of.

"To cut a long story short, Toyota says that its values are customer satisfaction first, then respect for employees and people development. Every company says something like this. But in this case, they walked the walk. The team leader got in a company van and came to talk directly to our operators about making assembly better for customers and easier for his team. D'you see? They could have gone the usual corporate complaint process, but chose a more direct way to demonstrate their values."

Delaney stared at the man, amazed. He had sounded so cagey when talking to her and Ward, but she suddenly saw what made him such as good supervisor. He was direct and friendly and shared his insights by telling a great story.

"The issue, then," Stevey said with a slow smile, "is to spell out what's most important for your company and what's most consistent with its values."

When no one spoke up, Delaney realized with a jolt what the problem was. The project manager was being consistent with what had been the most important thing in the company: don't lose another large client; go along with what they say. Cindy was protecting her relationship with her customer, who wanted to restrict access, rather than improve the product by consulting the actual users.

"What is most important is *making the best bloody software with the best bloody people*!" Delaney finally exclaimed. "Sharon is absolutely right. Cindy, come up with a plan to tackle the issue with the client and we'll discuss it together tonight. I'll go to bat personally with the client on this one if I have to, but I'd rather you try to solve it before getting me involved."

———

"I know what you're thinking," she said as she ushered Ward and Stevey in her office. "I shouldn't have put Cindy on the spot like that! And Mr. Davies, thank you for your inspired lesson. You were absolutely right, of course."

"Actually," Ward grinned, "that's not what I was thinking. You stepped in. You led. This is what we do. There's nothing in the job description that says you've got to be perfect. God knows I lose it with my guys as well. It's never easy to find the right balance between challenging and listening, and there are no guarantees about how people take it. In fact, I was thinking of the point I was trying to make in the car. Sharon was, in fact, demonstrating leadership."

"Sharon?" Delaney asked.

"Yes. We know how shy she is, but shy is just shy. She was convinced that her project manager was making a mistake. She had probably been holding her corner as best as she could when we came in, which was why the room felt so tense. And she spoke up to address the misalignment between you and ah—"

"Cindy."

"Cindy, right. Sharon was leading—not as a role, I don't know whether she could ever learn to take a formal leadership position—but situationally, personally. She believed in herself enough to stick to her guns, and believed you would listen to her, and that she could change the situation. She helped you reorient the team in the way you wanted. This is exactly the kind of leadership you should be trying to develop. This is what you need to succeed. And you demonstrated respect: you listened to her."

"But what about Cindy?" Jane wondered. "I did undercut her in front of every one."

"You did," Ward agreed. "And that's not good either, but don't be too hard on yourself. It's not like we want to be totally detached either. I find that the closer I am to the issue, the more likely I am to lose my temper and bark at someone. On topics where I have a lot more experience, it's easier to step back and take it slowly. It's hard to strike the right balance. Your involvement with issues is what brings energy to the company, but if you're too rough on people, you lose them.

"Cut yourself some slack, you'll do better next time. Focus on the fundamental problem: how to develop the kind of leadership from your staff that will support the company's growth."

Jane thought this over carefully. She was trying to identify who in Southcape was leading, whether in management or not. Terry Boyle came to mind immediately. The kid was a pain, but he was widely respected for his skill and the younger programmers did look up to him. Chris Williamson, maybe. Daniela, also maybe … but Sharon Miller? She really had to change her mind about that girl. This could explain why the loss of Simon Burnsell had barely been felt. She wondered how many of the project managers were leaders in Andy's terms. Any? Scary thought.

"But how do you develop leaders, then?" she asked.

"By doing what you're doing," he shrugged. "First, we manage for change and teach people to face different situations and solve problems, while keeping what is really important foremost. This is exactly what you've asked Cindy to do: Change her mind and come up with a plan to tackle a tricky situation, rather than work around it. Second, we *organize for learning*."

"What do you mean by that?"

"Well, we know that learning is individual. So we further define a job as:

$$JOB = WORK \text{ (WITH STANDARDS)} + KAIZEN$$

"Individuals get better at work by mastering standards and improve how they work with each other through kaizen. In order to facilitate this, we create a team environment to support this learning. Stevey, why don't you describe how you run your area?"

"Can't say that I do run it, really," Stevey replied. "My team leaders do mostly. As Mr. Ward was saying, every operator belongs to a stable team of five to seven people—five is ideal really. The important thing is that every operator knows that they belong to a team. Every team has a team leader. This leader still makes parts—he's not a boss or a manager, but a leader. The leader is with the team at all times, to make sure things run smoothly, that people understand standards, and that some kaizen is done to fix issues. Whenever anyone has a problem, the team leader stops what he or she's doing, and comes to give a hand. Either it can be sorted out right away and work continues, or if it can't, the leader calls me. Mr. Ward's main point is that while learning is individual, all learning occurs within the team.

"Every morning at the start of the shift, we have a five-minute get-together around the team leader."

"Like our standup meetings?"

"Nothing so fancy," he chuckled. "It's really just five minutes. Our American colleagues call it a 'huddle'—a term I can't get used to. For example, the team leader may have spotted something that didn't quite go right the day before and will tell the team members to pay attention to it during the day. Very often, it's about reminding the team about a standard. Mr. Ward calls it a daily teachable moment."

"The trouble is," Ward interjected, "some supervisors interpret this as a time to pass on management information to the workers. They completely miss the point. We don't want to get workers to participate in our management problems—they're not paid for that. We want supervisors, managers, and leaders to support workers in making good parts every day. So the meeting is really about workers."

"Checking one standard at a time?" Jane asked.

"Yeah," Stevey confirmed, "that, and listening to comments from operators. Just like Sharon was trying to do. I remind team leaders constantly to listen and to take what people tell them seriously. Listening is what glues the team together: They must feel they've got each other's back."

"Here," Andy said stepping to the board, "let me draw it out. Here's what our organization looks like (*below*) and this is how we define each minimum job role (*see page 172*)."

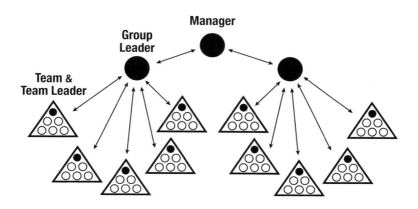

"Look," he explained. "Our performance is linked to how well we organize our value-adding teams, from the bottom up. We want to keep up standards, so we distinguish *okay* from *not okay*, and we always want to innovate to improve. I can't think of anyone who disagrees with that. But the reality of it is that often in our current

Minimum job roles at Nexplas

	Team Member	Team Leader	Supervisor
Safety	▓	▓	▓
Standardized work	▓	▓	▓
Remarking abnormalities	▓	▓	▓
Kaizen to eliminate waste in the cycle time	(dashed)	▓	▓
Eliminate variation in the flow of work		(dashed)	▓
Rebalancing the work flow			▓

state, we can't do either because we're not capable. People, equipment, methods, the whole supply chain. Nothing is quite at the right competence level to successfully sustain every standard."

"I'm with you," Jane nodded, thinking of the mess she'd progressively uncovered at Southcape.

"So to improve our ability to keep standards, we have to build our organizational capability to solve problems, learn, and change.

"Here," he said, picking up a whiteboard pen again and drawing a circle (*see right*). "The way we do it is by visualizing processes and reacting to abnormalities, then building up our problem-solving abilities, which eventually adds up to an organizational capability to solve problems. And this translates into process effectiveness—and hence superior operational performance and financial results."

"I guess we're doing that, as well," she said cautiously.

"Yep. And it's working. But you find it painfully slow and messy, and can't see how it might be scalable."

"*Touché.*"

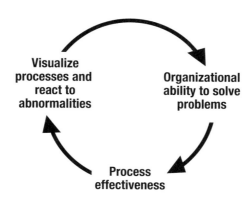

"It's all about people," Ward continued. "If you haven't got an organization built around people who can learn, and you're not clear on what they need to learn rather than what they want to learn, you're producing more heat than light. Relax. It's always messy. Look at our plant. The line management in place when we took over was there to staff, execute, and discipline. They were good people. They knew how to get the job done, no doubt about it. But what we look for are managers who can learn and teach. That's a completely different kind of person. So we had some good surprises, but we still have cases where they do what they do and won't learn. We don't know what to do with these people, and both sides end up frustrated with each other."

"Don't we just," added Stevey under his breath.

Delaney stared at Ward's scribblings thoughtfully.

"There's no avoiding it, I guess," she finally said, more to herself than anyone else. "I'm going to have to tackle standards—although I have no idea of how to do so."

"Dojos are the key," suggested Stevey helpfully. "That's how we got started. It gave everybody a place to examine the work, and the chance to participate in improvement by helping to define the best practices. Every supervisor commited 20 minutes a day to look at how people do the work and write the first standards."

Ward explained further, "I set up three programs when dealing with a new plant:

1. A go-and-see program to visit each gemba, get people to agree on what problems they have, and see how they get on.
2. A dojo program so that management takes responsibility to train each employee to the standards in their area.
3. A kaizen workshop program to get people to solve problems across organizational boundaries and improve processes.

"This is how we create a better dynamic between people, who learn from the dojos, to create better processes, and improve those processes through kaizen activities."

"I hear what you're saying: training, training, training. But what if they won't learn?" Jane complained.

"In the lean world," he grinned, "*if the student hasn't learned, the teacher hasn't taught*."

"And what if I train them and then they leave?"

"What if you don't and they stay?" he replied.

He'd taught her much, she thought, laughing at his reply.

Chapter Seven

INTENSIFY COLLABORATION

"Tell me, what happened?" Delaney asked Terry Boyle wearily. He barely bothered to look up from his laptop, leaning on his screen. She noted that he looked terrible, even by coder standards. He was unshaven and bleary eyed, and had skipped the usual smart-ass T-shirt for a gray hoodie with skulls and knives woven into a pattern—some band she didn't recognize.

She stifled a sigh, letting the silence last. The kid was one of their most gifted programmers and she had always been willing to give him a lot of leeway for his pain-in-the-butt attitude. She hated to think that her firm valued compliance over competence. But lately, he was slipping in terms of delivering code and responding to customer issues. There had been another incident at the client and his manager, Daniela, ever primed for drama, had stormed into her office asking for action. She didn't like the chap herself much, but was willing to give him a chance to tell his side of the story.

"Okay, mate, enough of this," she finally snapped. "Daniela told me something went wrong at the client site?"

"Yeah," he mumbled grudgingly. "She would."

"Well, she's your manager. It's her job. What happened?"

"Sure, it's her job to be on my back all the time."

This was not going to be easy.

"Listen, Terry, I can't help if I don't know the facts. Again, what happened?"

"Fire me for all I care," he snarled back, glaring at his computer.

"I don't intend to fire you," she said patiently. "And I don't want to see you firing yourself by making such a mess of things we have to choose between your head and the contract."

"Yeah, that'd cost the company a packet, wouldn't it?"

Money? Was that what this was about?

"Of course. But that's not the issue here. Look, it's pretty simple, really. You're one of our best programmers, and I for one would like to see you thrive with us."

"That's not what everybody thinks."

"Terry, what matters is what I am telling you right now. Please listen to me. Nobody wants you out of the job. And," she softened her tone slightly, "nobody wants to take this kind of action especially now, with the house and all." Earlier that year Boyle had asked for a raise as he was looking at buying a house with his fiancée. Delaney had not raised his pay, but had found enough justification to grant him a hefty bonus to help with the down payment.

"Yeah, well, that's not an issue now."

Oh.

"Okay, out with it," she said, trying to slow everything down and actively listen. "What's wrong?"

"Everything," he almost shouted, finally looking at her with pain and anger.

"The money doesn't matter because she's dumped me and I've had to give up the house and nobody cares what happens to me anymore and the clients are a 'wunch of bankers' and whatever I do Daniela keeps riding me and I've just had enough!"

Well, she thought, good to know. She paused before responding, cursing Daniela for not having warned her.

"I've been there," she finally said slowly. "And it hurts like hell, and nothing is going to make you feel better. I won't presume that I know exactly what you're feeling, but I can see that you've got serious matters on your mind. Do you want to take a few days? Do you want me to reassign you to another contract?"

Boyle looked back at his screen without answering for a while, finally shaking his head.

"No, I'll be fine," he finally sighed. "Work is the only thing that keeps me sane these days and I know I need to get a grip. If you get Daniela off my case, I'll do what I can to work with her and the client."

"I can certainly do that," she replied with relief. "I can ask her what's going on. Let's see how it goes and we can both think of another project if you can't see your way through this one."

"Thanks. I ... I appreciate it."

———

Jane had mixed feelings about this exchange when she sat back at her desk. She was relieved to have found out what was really going on with Boyle, and felt that she had succeeded at Ward's principle of treating him as an individual. But she felt daunted with the feeling that she had to carry the emotional weight of what everyone in her company was going through every day. She thought back to the shoe incident in Ward's plant. The operator had hurt her foot, but it had taken Ward—the European VP!—to get her managers to pay attention and help rather than discipline her.

She realized that her approach to this problem with Daniela was similar. Daniela had chosen to discipline Terry without trying to find out what was really going on. She made no great effort to understand his situation. She had not shown respect.

Jane was starting to figure out what 'treat each person as an individual' meant for her. Now she needed to teach her managers to do so as well. Lead with respect ... hmm ... She saw more clearly now that she got better results from people if she looked at every person as an individual. She had to accept that every person had their own reasons for doing what they did.

She'd learned a deep though painful lesson from Stevey (a front-line supervisor no less!) that again the problem was her. That in every

action she needed to demonstrate that she respected the core value of
Southcape: the best software for customers from the best programmers.

But how did she move it down the line? What did she expect from
Daniela? Pulling her tablet onto her lap, she drew a list. As a manager,
she expected Daniela to:

- deliver working systems without bugs
- handle the customer relationship
- find leads for new contracts
- reduce rework, in order to make money
- train top-notch coders
- keep her teams' spirits up
- deal with all the day-to-day incidents

But also:

- help her with staffing correctly to manage growth
- keep an open eye for new technologies they should
  develop and investigate
- and obviously, show respect

Quite a list, really. Now, on the other hand, Terry would have a
different list of issues. Something like:

- his job
- his love life (or family, for older staff)
- his health
- his aspirations, money, career, so forth
- his background—he certainly had a chip on his shoulder
  about *something*.

What could she do to align both? More to the point, how could
she train her line managers to align the company's needs with
employees' needs? She drew two circles, splitting these demands as pie
charts and stared at them, reflecting on all that she had learned from
Ward. Lead with respect covered so much ground: defining success,

respecting people's autonomy, developing relationships by developing individual skills in problem solving with others.

She drew with purpose now a triangle:

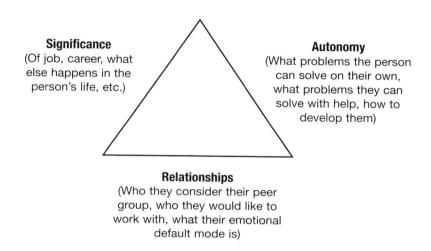

Significance
(Of job, career, what else happens in the person's life, etc.)

Autonomy
(What problems the person can solve on their own, what problems they can solve with help, how to develop them)

Relationships
(Who they consider their peer group, who they would like to work with, what their emotional default mode is)

She stared at the resulting diagram, convinced that she was on to something, and thinking back on Ward's point that the company was its people. She needed to put this into practice now and Daniela was as good a starting point as any. But oh, how that woman could drive her crazy!

———————

"I've given some thought to that obsession of yours with our delivery—how do you say—lead time?" said Rob, his mouth full of scampi and linguini. "I'm not sure we can think so globally."

Jane sought her inner smile, thankful for her yoga practice. 'Listen to the man,' she admonished herself. At least he had started coming to the Wednesday lunches with her and Mike. The tradition was slowly reestablishing itself.

"Seems to me we have four different types of activities. We have large implementation projects. We have module design for platform customization to specific requests. We have the weird stuff where clients don't know what they want. And then we have applications maintenance."

"Our four value streams, yes," she nodded thoughtfully.

"If you want," he shrugged, throwing back some more wine. "We can't just look at an average lead-time, it's meaningless. Each type of project has its own lead-time."

"Yes, but the overall lead-time tells us how we fare with our responses to customers in general. Still, it's a good point, we can easily look at each of these value streams and measure how well we respond."

"If you want us to be very good at some things, we should ask ourselves the question by, uh, value streams. What's more, I've been thinking …"

'Hear, hear!' she thought snidely, carefully keeping her expression neutral.

"What should Sales be very good at? Obviously, asking this question does not mean that I'm saying we're bad. I'm thinking about this in the spirit of general improvement. I accept that we don't just want contracts—we want contracts when we have the capacity to do them. See, I can listen as much as the next man. Second, we could always define the customer needs better. That's true of any sales organization. Third, we could probably learn to steer customers more toward off-the shelf solutions, if there is such a thing."

She raised her eyebrows appreciatively. No mention of improving Sales' response time or working better with the rest of the outfit. But at least some thinking about improvement. Score a major step forward.

"I like the idea that we discussed last time of having a sales pace. I wondered what our sales pace should be for each of those four value streams. So I've looked back historically and, give or take, we seem to be making two or three big implementations a year. We deliver about a hundred modules a year, and about the same in special projects.

on systematic ET

Maintenance is more or less ongoing. So if I think in terms of pace, this means a big project every six months, a module every three days, and a special project every three days. I've been wondering how we should go about selling at this kind of rhythm. No idea how so far, but it's an interesting way of looking at it."

"I don't know either," she answered, "but this is fascinating stuff, Rob. I am convinced that you're going about it the right way, and am curious to see where that leads …"

His comments had triggered another chain of thought. With the acquisition of the new firm now almost complete, she'd been wondering how to organize the expanded company. Historically, her belief that so-called flat organizations were most effective made her wary of putting a middle-management structure in place.

She originally thought that she could handle the project leaders directly. Increasingly, she'd come to admit this wasn't working, She simply didn't have time to give them the attention they required, particularly with all the problem emphasis of this past year. She had been puzzling over how to create a middle-manager structure that would reflect 'organizing for learning' and she wondered whether Rob's value-stream idea was the correct way to skin that particular cat. She would look into it, but suspected that the skills that made you good at large projects were not the same as what was needed for ad hoc computing requests.

———

"May I change the topic?" Mike asked, though of course there was no chance of refusing. "I have a surprise for you," he said, boyishly waving his hands in the air like a conjurer. "You are hereby invited to the first session of Southcape University, which will be held this Friday at 2 p.m. in the conference room," he announced grandly.

"What—"

"You said carte blanche!" he cut in, tapping his nose.

181

"Sure I did, but—"

"I've been having so much fun with this confirmation process," he continued. "But, the proles are suffering. They find the problem-solving process, shall we say, rigorous. So I thought of a way to make it more part of what we do. I've asked one of our developers to stand up every Friday in front of the gang and present how they tackled a particular problem."

"If you think that speaking in front of their peers will be seen as an incentive," Rob laughed loudly, "you're as daft as you look."

"It's about doing it together," Mike continued undisturbed. "It's about making problem solving part of our culture, part of who we are."

"As well as making sure they take it seriously," nodded Jane, secretly pleased that both her partners had launched initiatives to support what she was trying to do. It didn't really matter so much whether things worked or not. What mattered was that they had taken these initiatives. They could always improve them as they went along.

"Should be interesting. So they're going to stand up and present, is that it?" she asked.

"Not quite, they'll be presenting an A3."

"A3?" sniggered Rob. "That's a lean thing, right?"

"Shush, I don't want to spoil the surprise!"

For once, she and Rob looked at each other in agreement, and rolled their eyes, equally annoyed and amused.

———

"How's the book going, by the way?" she asked Mike as they made their way back to the offices.

"Good, thank you, jolly good. I'm getting quite a bit of media attention. Maybe even a TED talk. But that's old hat now. I'm already working on the next one."

"Oh?"

"Absolutely, you see when I wrote *Big Data Is Here* about how computers exchange data sets, how they'll optimize their own operations, and what it means for humans, I thought I'd written all I'd ever had to say. You know, connectivity, real-time, data-driven. But now, I want to write about the human use of IT systems. I think I'll call it, *Beyond Intuition*.

"You see, working on confirmation is endlessly fascinating. I suspect that the developers loathe it but I am convinced that there's real value to this—to see how intuition works and to push people to think beyond their first response. I honestly thought data management was going to take over solving human problems, but the power of the human mind ... Janey! It's unbelievable!"

"Really?" She was a bit worried by so much enthusiasm.

"They really surprise you, they do. Once you're past the usual crap, they start thinking of things I hadn't thought about. I'm amazed by the innovation potential. It's 'Oh Wow!' material. Truly."

———————

By the time they reached the office Jane couldn't contain herself any longer.

"Look, Mike, you know how I hate surprises. Let's go to my office and preview what you've cooked up for Friday."

She was surprised to hear that he'd looked up lean and problem solving and discovered a full methodology. He then made the astonishing step of going to a training session—himself, Mike, the famous pundit and knower of all things.

"It's a method of problem solving called an A3," he explained excitedly. "The idea is that a full problem-solving story should fit onto an A3 piece of paper."

"A3, as in the paper size?"

"Yes, the paper you find in the copy-machine. It's the largest piece of paper we have around the office." He rummaged around her office as if it were his own, found a large sheet of paper with writing on the front, turned it over, and began sketching on the back.

"First, *clarify the problem*. You need to visualize the gap between what's actually happening and the ideal situation. The idea is to find the measure that best represents the problem, and show historically and graphically where you are and where you want to be. If we can't do that, we don't understand the problem well enough to solve it.

"Second, *break down the problem*. This is about drawing out the process generating the situation we're looking at, identifying exactly where things go wrong, and listing potential factors. You're supposed to test every factor to confirm which one has the greatest impact on the problem.

"Third, *set a target*. Once you've figured out the factor having the biggest impact on performance, you can set a performance target, aim for total eradication of this factor, and guesstimate what impact it would have on the indicator. This also gives you a due date.

"Fourth, *seek root cause*. Why is the main factor occurring? You ask why repeatedly until you find a cause that is so large that it's outside your immediate action range. The idea is to find the most fundamental thing that we can affect rapidly, and focus on it.

"Fifth, *develop a number of countermeasures*. If you can only come up with one solution you haven't understood the problem fully—or you're jumping to the one solution you're comfortable with, which may be second best. You need to force yourself to explore different routes to address the root cause and then pick the one that's going to follow through on the basis of impact and cost.

"Six, *follow through*. Plan the implementation of your counter-measures and make sure all happens on plan. If something gets off track, you need to see this early and ask why? Maybe you've missed something, or maybe the commitment to solve the problem is lagging.

"Seven, *check the results and the process*. Are you getting the expected results? Have you done what you planned to do? I guess that's what you'd call confirmation.

A3 Problem-solving sheet

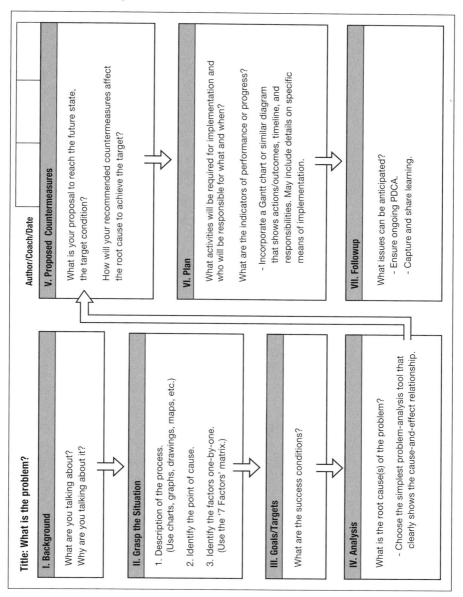

Author/Coach/Date

Title: What is the problem?

I. Background

What are you talking about?
Why are you talking about it?

II. Grasp the Situation

1. Description of the process.
   (Use charts, graphs, drawings, maps, etc.)

2. Identify the point of cause.

3. Identify the factors one-by-one.
   (Use the '7 Factors' matrix.)

III. Goals/Targets

What are the success conditions?

IV. Analysis

What is the root cause(s) of the problem?

- Choose the simplest problem-analysis tool that clearly shows the cause-and-effect relationship.

V. Proposed Countermeasures

What is your proposal to reach the future state, the target condition?

How will your recommended countermeasures affect the root cause to achieve the target?

VI. Plan

What activities will be required for implementation and who will be responsible for what and when?

What are the indicators of performance or progress?

- Incorporate a Gantt chart or similar diagram that shows actions/outcomes, timeline, and responsibilities. May include details on specific means of implementation.

VII. Followup

What issues can be anticipated?
- Ensure ongoing PDCA.
- Capture and share learning.

Adapted from Shook and Verble, *Managing to Learn.*

185

"Eight, *adjust or standardize*. How do you make sure these results will hold? What else do you need to fix to make sure the new process will be sustained? What issues remain open? And does what you've learned apply elsewhere?

"And it all fits on an A3 sheet of paper, to formalize learning and communicate it easily (*see page 185*)."

"On one single sheet? How does that help?" she asked.

"That's the brilliance of it!" he laughed, having his fun. "It's a great communication tool. Look on top here, besides the title, we have several boxes," he explained as he drew. "They're for sign-offs by the A3 author and coach, and the date. The point of these A3 sheets is not the problem-solving structure, it's the fact that the sheet supports a structured problem-solving conversation between two people."

"Um …"

"Say I coach you—heaven forbid—on how to use the cloud to store your personal data."

She raised an eyebrow and gave him her best forbidding stare.

"First, we would have to agree on a problem title, which is far harder than you'd think. Then we have to agree on the problem definition—what is the gap to standard. This means agreeing on what is the standard, ideal, etc., what is the current situation, and how we're going to measure this. No mean thing!

"Then, we have to agree on what are the most influential factors, how we tested each of them, and how we've confirmed our hunches. Then we have to agree on a meaningful target. Too low and there's no challenge to look for breakthrough ideas; too high and it's unrealistic. Then we have to agree on what we consider the root cause.

"Then we have to agree on what alternative actions we can think up, and which one we'll chose to have a go at. Then we have to put a plan together and get it done. Then we have to agree on what impact our efforts have had and what effects we can see. Then we have to agree on what conclusions to draw from the entire exercise.

"It may sound formal, and perhaps mechanical, until you try it and discover the intuitive aspect and power of the process. I see it as a great platform for innovation—a way to develop basic skills that enable the individuals to learn and develop mastery—like a musician doing scales and exercises. The beauty of the A3 is that while an author is using it to explore and learn on their own, as the coach, I can steer them through the process, challenge their assumptions, and open up unseen options."

"It does sound impressive," she agreed cautiously.

"The elegance of it is that this one-page document should read as a simple story that can be shared more widely to other stakeholders to see whether they agree on the thinking, or whether we're missing something big."

"And you've completed some of these A3s?"

"The proof is in the pudding. Daniela Webb is presenting hers tomorrow, we'll see how that goes."

"Daniela?" Jane asked, surprised.

"Who likes easy challenges?" Mike tittered.

———

Friday afternoon arrived. Jane stood at the back of a crowded conference room, watching Daniela sweat through the presentation of her problem: developing the practice of autotesting within Southcape. She had carefully gone through the eight steps of the problem-solving methodology and was outlining what she thought were the three root causes of slow adoption. First, autotesting was a skill that few had mastered. Second, they had speed issues, because if the tests took more than 30 minutes nobody bothered with them. And third, they were plagued with so many legacy issues with the applications they ran that one often didn't know where to start testing.

Jane was impressed. She had always found Daniela somewhat flaky, but seeing her go through the step-by-step method was a credit to Mike's tutoring. She had been so focused on her issues with Rob that she had underestimated the good fortune of having Mike take to this problem-solving stuff so quickly. He'd even offered to oversee the entire project review schedule—which sparked a bit of an argument, as she wanted project managers to remain in control of their review schedules. He had sidestepped her by imposing code-review sessions, much like David had done, except with better planning.

The conference room was starting to get hot and stuffy, and she worried that people were finding the exercise to be dragging on. Few seemed all that excited. But it didn't matter, really. This was a brilliant idea regardless.

She had a suddenly fanciful notion that she was forging her firm together, with heat from the room and hammering from Daniela, she thought with a mental smile. Yes, she would have to make sure they'd keep to this regularly—whether people liked it or not. Yes, she liked this image. She would be forging the company together by getting each of them to stand up and present in front of everyone else. This repeated practice would create teamwork by getting one person to take the lead in working with the others.

She noticed that she was standing right behind Terry, who was back to his normal irritating self. Talking with Daniela had helped and he had somehow pulled through. He was trying to text discreetly. His T-shirt said: *The trouble with real life is there is no danger music.*

It was like working with human-sized fortune cookies. She should have some *Why? Why? Why?* T-shirts made. Maybe then the punks would take her seriously, though Terry would more than likely wear one that said *Because. Because. Because.*

It didn't matter. She was really pleased with what she was seeing. Southcape was finally taking concrete steps to strengthen relationships within the firm. The 'university' defined them all as belonging to the same thinking workplace and exchanging real knowledge together. She felt she was finally getting a handle on leading with respect.

————

It was a balmy late summer evening and Jane sat relaxed in her narrow garden, enjoying the scent of sunburned grass, browsing the web until she'd finally found what she had at the back of her mind.

There! She smiled to herself as she read the page on her tablet. 'Standards and kaizen' had been nagging at her since her visit to the Swindon plant, a teasing memory that she couldn't place. But now she'd nailed it down—she *had* come across something like this before.

Before joining David's venture, she had briefly worked in the bank's training department, helping to develop training courses for bank tellers to use the new IT systems that would, in the ensuing years, largely replace them. She'd hated every minute of it!

She remembered that the fad then had been "action learning." Classroom teaching was out, action learning was in. Every workshop had to be thought of as hands-on experience, not unlike Ward's lean, she thought wryly. Now she was looking at the foundational equation (yes, equation!) of action learning:

$$\text{LEARNING} = \text{PROGRAMMED KNOWLEDGE} + \text{INSIGHT QUESTIONING}$$

Programmed knowledge meant all the formal instruction of what is explicitly known. Insight questioning concerned the posing of questions to trigger insights and deeper understanding of the subject matter. This was the thought that had been nagging her: the balance between standards and kaizen.

Andy would probably scoff at her for over-intellectualizing, but it helped her to look at things from different perspectives. Even as a parent she realized that her approach had shifted subtly. She managed her daughters less these days and listened more, tried to share more, model more, and back their decisions with respect. Somehow she was forcing things less and, to be honest, enjoying them more.

She now had a better handle on his three programs: go-and-see visits to understand the context of value creation, dojos to spread the programmed knowledge, and kaizen workshops to spur insight questioning. Somehow, it was coming together.

After Daniela, Cindy Munn had been another surprise. The stubborn woman hadn't budged much about formal problem solving. She still felt the procedure was a waste of time and that as a manager she was supposed to solve problems for her teams. But she'd taken to standards like a duck to water!

She was the first manager at Southcape to take up the dojo idea. Leery from previous total quality attempts, she had focused on the very narrow core tasks that programmers did every day, such as naming variables, file paths, logic conventions, table structures, etc.—things that they all assumed a programmer should know how to do on his or her own. She had uncovered enormous variation of practices, and many sources of mistakes and misunderstandings. She got her team together to agree on some basic ways to do the most frequent steps. She proudly held up a yellow folder—paper, not computer—with the standards her team had agreed on.

Jane was thrilled, seeing beyond the measly six paper sheets to the very core of their competence: how to write code. This was the first time since she'd started her lead with respect journey that she'd actually touched the heart of the job.

––––––––––

Not in a thousand years would Jane have thought she'd know her way around a production shop floor. But as she stood with Ward and some of his managers next to the supply racks in a production cell, she no longer felt like a fish out of water. Ward had intended to show her something else, but had gotten embroiled in yet another 'teachable moment' with his staff. She now understood that there were some things he could not walk past without reacting.

"It's within regulations, but it is heavy," grunted Len Barton, straining as he hefted a plastic container in his hands. "And, yes, I agree we shouldn't have stored this so low because it will strain operators' backs."

"Why?" asked Ward, scowling.

Barton and Tim Russon, the logistics supervisor Jane had met on her first visit to the plant, stood there looking aggrieved.

"Because we've got to make it all bloody well *fit*," Tim finally said, exasperated. "This is our first attempt at making a flat-storage supermarket so that the supply train can come and pick up straight from here—and we know we just have too much stock in there."

Delaney's guess was that Tim, under pressure from Barton to get it done for Ward's visit, had simply come up with a quick-fix solution. Now he was being taken to task for not having paid enough attention to ergonomics. Ward was clearly struggling to keep his temper.

"Why?" asked Ward again, with exaggerated patience.

"I know where you're going with this," retorted Barton. "You're thinking that, once more, we've put the plant ahead of the people. I'm not defending it, but we've got to *run* this plant, for Pete's sake."

"I know you do, and you do it well," said Ward. "But we rearrange logistics shelves once every blue moon, while the operators will have to bend over and pick up the lower row of boxes every day, repeatedly. We've got to show we care!" he said adamantly, shaking his head.

"It's good that you created a supermarket, but you didn't need to do it all at once, did you? Guys, hear me! People come first. End of story, all right?" Ward said firmly. "There's no rush, you're doing fine. Keep to the basics and kaizen. And when you do kaizen, work with the operators to fix ergonomics problems first. People don't come to work to hurt themselves. Got it?"

"I'm on it, guv," sighed Tim, who with a sidelong glance shared an elaborate silent conversation with the plant manager. "We'll pull the kaizen team together and close the lower shelf level, so that the supply-train guys won't have to bend down so low. I know, I know, the ideal is that every box moves horizontally without carrying, just pushing. I'm with you there. We just need to learn how to do it."

"Change is never easy," conceded Ward. "And both of you are doing a great job. It's just galling when we make mistakes like this that could undermine all the trust we're slowly building with the team members. Remember it takes years to grow a tree, and a few minutes to chop it down, right?"

Ward turned to Delaney as the two other men nodded and left them to get on with fixing what they'd just implemented. "Sorry about that, Jane. Did you pick up what I wanted you to see here?"

She knew she should be used to this sort of question by now, but she still bristled at being put on the spot. At least she had learned not to react.

"Actually, no. Show me?"

"Look, over here in these supermarket racks. We have short lead-time parts from our local suppliers that we pick up regularly with a milk run. Our trucks go around to their facilities on a standard route and pick up a small quantity of everything every day, which we then store in these shelves over here. Do you see those tall racks over there? They hold long lead-time items that come from Asia, which we need to recondition first before putting them on the lines. And then over there are rare parts we get in when we need, on and off, and so on."

"You don't have a single system dealing with all your components, is that what you're saying?"

"That's it. And we need our database structure to be able to cope with this. Chris is doing a good job, but he is still thinking in terms of a one-size-fits-all system. I need you to understand that different lead-time conditions make us deal with suppliers differently, and that we need to have that flexibility in the IT system. We need space for change. Do you understand?"

"I hear you, but it might not be so easy from an IT point of view."

"I realize that," he replied testily. "However, this is not a 'but' situation, it's an 'and.' I am not asking for miracle solution, but I am expecting a problem statement that states the issue clearly. Nina will not green-light the next phase of development until I'm satisfied we're all very clear on what we're trying to tackle here."

"Got it. I'll talk to Chris and we'll come up with a list of the key issues the system should address by the end of the week."

Had he said next phase? Delaney wondered. Were they really considering an upgrade as Chris had said? She started to see why he kept repeating that the goalposts moved. It seemed that every time they'd crack an issue, something else came up. Was that what kaizen was all about?

"I've been remiss," apologized Ward, as he walked her out.

"How so?"

"Go and see," he answered, with a guilty grimace. "I've not visited Southcape nearly as often as I should. How are you doing?"

"We've been working hard at teaching problem solving and standards," she said. "Hard balance to find."

"Tell me about it!" he agreed. "Without standards, it's hard to see problems clearly, and without problem solving, standards are not taken seriously. It's like the palm and back of the hand; you can't get one without the other. That exchange I just had in logistics reminds me that we need to look together to see whether we agree on what we mean and intend.

"It gets very tiresome sometimes—you saw those two chaps back there," he griped. "But it always steers us back to the implications of *lead with respect*. Problem solving is essential, but we're also trying to build mutual respect. Mutual respect with customers by making our best effort to understand what they value, and mutual respect with employees by offering them satisfaction in their work.

"The prerequisites are stable and improving relationships. But the difficulty is that we must say things as we see them and put problems first. So we need to find ways to talk to each other where people can face problems without going ballistic. We're all human, so tempers often get in the way."

"Don't they just," she agreed, laughing. She'd had her fair share of outbursts at Southcape, but over the summer things had seemed to smooth over as people got used to the new way of looking at work. She was more tolerant of Ward's manner, too, now that she realized that what had first appeared to be arrogance and bluntness masked his own struggles with finding the best way to lead and learn.

"You have to take care of people," he said for the second time that day. "You can't develop them if you don't care. The culture of *lead with respect* is based on the fact that when unfavorable information is passed on we—the management—pay earnest regard to it and act upon it, right?"

"Honestly, I get that part," she answered. "However, I really struggle with making my own managers understand it. When you start to dig into work problems, many of them end up being personal problems. I realize that I've got to teach my managers to see personal issues as part of the problem, but I'm really struggling there. How far should we go?"

Ward hesitated, then said, "In some ways the best action is no action—at first. We work hard to train middle managers to take thoughtful action by understanding people's individual situation, rather than respond immediately by looking for blame. We believe that good relationships bring good results. It's obvious I guess, but in practice, keeping good relationships in a supervisory situation is hard. Every case in which a supervisor feels she has to *take action* can be defined as a problem and solved with more foresight, rather than putting employees in their place or kick the buck up the line.

"So our practice is:
   - Get the facts
   - Weigh and decide
   - Take action
   - Check results"

Jane commiserated by sharing, "My main issue is that my managers jump the gun every time—and end up in sticky messes that I usually have to clean up. So, back to training case-by-case, I guess. Is this a standard?"

"I guess it is," Ward grinned. "But don't lose sight of the awesome potential of it—the vision of developing every person to the fullest of their abilities and involving them in running and improving their own workplaces."

"Look," he said, pointing to the wall of the lobby. "They finally got it going."

Across the wall she could see a banner saying "Suggestion of the Month" with plaques beneath with silver stars and names on them.

"Every month a site committee picks the best suggestion from the implemented suggestions that supervisors report to it. This is often simple, menial stuff, but we can finally put on display that we are proud of our team members' efforts to contribute.

"See, this is what I get a kick out of," he continued, surprisingly passionate. "I love it when a person has taken an idea, project, or suggestion all the way to doing it, and they can see their personal contribution to the company. They can say: Look at this. I did that."

"Suggestion of the month, not employee of the month?"

"Employee of the month would mean we put someone forward for who they are," he replied with a quick frown.

"Remember we constantly have to deal with the fact that you can't stop petty bosses from rewarding their mates and punishing those they dislike. We're not rewarding the person for their compliance; we're recognizing their contribution to the company, the community. That's a big difference, in my opinion.

"The operator gets a plaque, Barton shakes their hand as we put it up, and they get a modest reward such as gift coupons as recognition.

We don't want to monetize suggestions because thinking at work is part of the job, but we still want to show our appreciation.

"To my mind," he continued, "the spirit of *lead with respect* begins with figuring out what really matters, so that we don't have people improving the efficiency of actions that aren't important in the first place. Our job as executives is to find the high-impact topics and let our employees deal with everything else. Our job is to help train and develop every person to contribute to these key subjects, by learning to do their jobs better and better every day. Not just when there's a big crisis and they can be hero firefighters, but during the day-to-day grind.

"The spirit of respect comes down to kaizen—coming up with new ways of doing things, testing them, convincing colleagues, so that any one person can be proud of what they've brought to the party. In so many places I've worked at in the past, people looked at the future with fear, and the past with anger.

"My dream is to create a place where we look at the future with hope and the past with pride—with the satisfaction of a job well done. But none of this is possible if we don't learn to build mutually respectful relationships first. This is what we need to teach to every one, every day."

Ward looked down after this speech, sheepish at having delivered yet another lecture. "Come on, then," he said lightly, "time to get you on your way."

"Okay," said Ward, intrigued, "show me."

"The screen over there," replied Barton, pointing toward a large flat-screen on the wall where the procurement staff sat.

"Is that the current status of the milk-run trucks?" he asked, impressed.

"It is," Nina Miah answered. "Each line shows a truck route. You can see whether the pick-up status is *green* (okay) or *red* (not okay) and the truck's estimated arrival time back at the factory. It's like a train-station display board."

"How …?"

"The Southcape laddie cobbled it together," Barton answered with one of his tight-lipped smiles. "Before driving off from the supplier, the driver ticks off his pick-up list and phones into an automated system. The driver taps 1 for *okay* or 2 for *missing parts*. It's rough and doesn't do anything but record whether the delivery is complete or not, and the time of departure, but it gives us a real-time view of our pick-ups."

"And good kaizen opportunities," added Nina. "We've realized that we had ignored traffic conditions when we organized the truck routes. It's obvious in hindsight, but we didn't understand why some routes had so much more variation than others. Since we've got this up, we've actually started listening to the drivers."

"Good stuff," Ward said happily. "I've never seen this counter-measure before. And that's why you think they're ready?" he asked, looking at them both.

"You know we need to upgrade our systems," Barton said.

"As I stated in my A3, I agree with Len," Nina said. "We knew all along the IT system was holding us back and creating a lot of wasted work. We didn't know how to go forward. I think that all the work the Southcape team has done gives us a pretty good idea of what we want."

"It's a rather big job." And a good chunk of cash Ward thought without saying it.

Barton and Nina looked at each other again.

"Your decision," he told them. "I'm sure you realize the amount of work and hassle a system upgrade involves. Your call."

They nodded as one.

Ward really didn't look forward to the mess a large-scale IT system change would create, but if they were confident he would support them. But above all, he was happy that the two had agreed on the proposal. A year ago, they barely said hello when they met and opposed each other on every topic, production-versus-purchasing-kind-of things, with logistics being the main bone of contention.

He'd had to bang their heads together more than once, reminding himself that win-win didn't necessarily mean nice-nice. Eventually Len had mellowed a little, and Nina had got her head around the logistics of procurement, not just purchasing. She'd done a splendid job and he wondered whether she'd be game for the division-level purchasing role that remained vacant. Though if he promoted her, he had a good idea which crony Len would want in the vacated slot in the plant, Ward thought with a mental sigh. Oh, well, that's a fight for another day. And maybe Len would surprise him in the end.

———

"Cindy! Here's to you!" Delaney said happily, raising a glass of bubbly. "You've done it!"

"Hear, hear!" chimed in Mike, heartily toasting the pleased and slightly bewildered Cindy Munn.

Even Rob was putting a good face on it, although she'd fairly pulled the carpet from under his feet. The three partners had invited her to lunch at Giovanni's to celebrate her landing a major contract to handle the entire response process of a large bank—from the help desk to server maintenance. Best of all, this get was never even formally identified as a goal.

"How did you swing it?" asked Mike, draining his glass and immediately refilling it.

"I don't know, really," stammered Cindy. She was rather assertive as a rule, but seemed unusually lost for words. "It just sort of happened."

"What did? Regale us with a tale!" he insisted.

Jane kept quiet—she already knew the story. Sipping the sweet, sparkling prosecco, she tasted again the surprise and the excitement she'd felt when Cindy had outlined the opportunity—and how good it had felt to tell her to run with it, rather than take over as she'd had no doubt done in the past.

"Well ... it started with the work on dojos. It drove me crazy that people couldn't just keep standards. I was going on with the 20-minute daily training and the same problems as when we tried Total Quality. It was not that they didn't know the standards—they would just do something else. Drove me nuts.

"And then it hit me. What that production chap from Nexplas lectured us on, actually. Whenever my guys were not following standards, they had reasons—their reasons for sure, but reasons all the same. They didn't see that standards were not rules to be followed but rather the right way to work—even in difficult conditions. Standards were the uphill flag we had to measure up to and strive to achieve."

"Vivid image," murmured Rob, unexpectedly civil.

"Yes, thanks. This is what I was missing about problem solving. We had to learn to solve problems in order to apply standards. So I had to understand the problems people encountered that stopped them from applying standards, and help them deal with these issues, so that following standards would be easier.

"Don't laugh," she grinned at Jane. "I did change my mind. I started going through the problem-solving training just the way I did with the standards training. I realized they went together.

"Now we were working on one big application for the bank. Since we're doing all this work as a team our delivery improves and we start solving all these problems for the bank guys. Then one day I noticed that they kept bitching about the time it took to solve tickets on the complaints hotline. I didn't listen much at first, because our own application was causing fewer problems and we were solving those much faster. But the bank IT guy was complaining about all their applications, not just ours.

"Not my problem, I thought," she admitted ruefully. "But then I remembered a chat I had with Jane? About how one of your objectives was to make more innovative offers to customers? About bringing back the sense of fun you guys had when you started the company?"

The three directors exchanged side-looks.

"And I then thought—what the hell, let's take a chance. So I went out on a limb and told my contact at the bank that we could reduce the number of problems on the other applications just as we'd done on ours if they would give us enough control. She said, 'Okay, start with one,' which we did—and luckily, we showed some quick results. Suddenly, she turns around and suggests that we take over the entire process, from help-desk to maintenance of their four main applications. And voilà."

Mike and Rob peppered Cindy with detailed questions on how she planned to go forward. Jane stayed quiet, reeling at the promise suddenly shown by her, whose obsession about procedures and zero initiative had previously pegged her as middle manager for life.

Jane had been considering pitching the client for full-process outsourcing, but no opportunity had ever really come up. Cindy's initiative had opened up new ground to challenge her strategic thinking. She couldn't think of a clearer case of achieving her growth objectives by developing someone.

She also saw the clear-cut illustration of the power of catchball. She had somehow convinced Cindy that she could make a difference to the firm and for herself—the elusive sweet spot between the company's fortunes and individual fulfillment.

It was all good. Better than good, it was unexpectedly great! And in truth, beyond Daniela and Cindy, several frontline coders such as Chris, Terry, and Sharon were also showing enormous promise.

Still, she remained unsettled by the contingent nature of this way of working. Sure, the contract Cindy landed would simply not have happened in the old way of running Southcape. But she used to have a clearer idea of what was going on—she made decisions, people implemented them, and she could directly control how things were going. Now ... she saw that her results were really built by people and dependent on them.

Scary thought—or hopeful. Be an optimist for once, she chided herself. Good things can happen, and although nothing is ever easy, setbacks are just problems to solve. They can and will be overcome as long as she succeeded in aligning value for customers and individual success. The real question was: how many Cindy Munns did she have in the company whose potential she had not spotted—right under her very nose?

"Andy? It's Jane. I wanted to call to thank you. I have Nina's purchase order on my desk."

"Don't thank me," he laughed on the phone. "I was set against it, but Nina and Len ganged up on me."

"I mean, thank you for everything. We just had a Southcape shareholder meeting and our numbers have never been better."

"Excellent! You can give us a good price for the systems revamp."

"We will. Seriously, what you taught me has completely changed the company's growth trajectory."

"That's good to hear—but we're hardly done. We need to get this upgrade right without screwing up operations."

"I promise we won't let you down. Also, I think I've had a flash of insight. We've been applying the problem-solving tools for a while now on a wide variety of topics. I've been wondering, how come in some cases people come up with really clever countermeasures, but in others they just seem to go through the motions and whatever they come up with is simply not very interesting?"

"Yep, I get that, as well. And?"

"Well, I've been looking at it case-by-case, and what I think I've realized is that the quality of the solution rests on the intensity of the collaboration on the problem solving. I can't think of a better way to explain it."

Ward was suddenly quiet.

"Wrong answer?"

"No, not at all!" he exclaimed. "As I think about it, I do believe you're right. It's the quality of the teamwork that produces the quality of the countermeasure. Yes. Absolutely …"

"So it makes sense then?"

"It makes perfect sense!" he agreed excitedly. "I'm thinking about the problems I'm looking into now and yes, in some cases the guys come together and try many ideas and come up with something smart and unexpected. But in other cases they just fill in the paperwork and nothing much comes out it."

"Yes, I've realized that I can help clarify the problems, but how to help intensify the collaboration remains mysterious. Sometimes my people work together and excitedly build on each other's ideas, and other times they keep talking past each other. Personalities, maybe?"

"I simply don't know," he acknowledged, "I really need to think about it. Thank you for pointing this out. See! The learner becomes the teacher. My hunch is that you're absolutely right. I like the way you put it, we have to find a way to intensify collaboration."

"I had another question," she said, quietly pleased by his comment about her teaching him something for a change—it had been long in coming!

"Sure, shoot."

"I've learned so much this past year. But I was wondering: did you learn something, as well?"

"Of course … ah. Lots, let me see …"

"If you don't …"

"It's fine. Give me a second to think about it," Ward said, as he tried to organize his thoughts. "The first thing that comes to mind is that I've completely changed my mind about IT. I used to think it was a necessary evil. You know, I only heard about it when it crashed.

It was something we couldn't do without, but that it came burdened with legacy costs, awkward systems, boxes full of obsolete stuff, and software we never knew how to use—you know what I mean.

"But I've come to realize how strategic IT is to the business, and how increasingly it's going to be the business. And I'm not just talking ERPs and e-mails. I've been paying more attention to our engineering software and the communication difficulties we experience, and I'm wondering whether we could create a more open-source environment within the company. I expect I'll be picking your brains about this pretty soon."

"I'll have to introduce you to Mike Wembley," she said. "I'm sure he'll have some very interesting ideas to share."

"With pleasure. The second thing I've learned, is that supplier relationships go way beyond improving transactions. I suspect that's why Phil challenged me to work on supplier development. Working with you I've come to realize that if I see suppliers as allies I can benefit from their innovation and inventiveness. This has been a big step for me. It goes well beyond the IT work we've been involved with. I can see now that some of my key suppliers can help me see new product innovations, if I can have the right conversation with them, which in the past I've never even tried."

"Do you mean suggestions from suppliers?" she asked.

"Kinda, yes—you're right. Creating the kind of relationship with suppliers where they understand the kind of questions I have, and I have enough understanding of what they do to trust my judgment about the solutions they come up with. Yes, similar to suggestions. Spot on."

"And about lead with respect? Anything?"

"You mean other than discovering how pompous I sound when I lecture?" he laughed. "Let me see. The underlying model I have about lead with respect balances challenging with listening, teaching problem solving with engaging, and finally, developing teamwork with learning. What I see is how much I can learn from studying the countermeasures people come up with when they solve problems—if I give them a freer hand. So I'm asking myself: what is Swindon teaching me?

"The bigger picture is somehow to mesh the company's development with individual fulfillment. This means that as a leader I have to translate larger organizational changes into specific changes in people's jobs. As the boss, it's easy to see how I can define the challenges, and then teach others to change their roles and learn to do things differently.

"What I underestimated is how much I had to learn from doing that. External change is always faster than internal change. That's something Phil is very attuned to. But I'm not, not really. For instance, changing my mind about the role of IT also radically changes the scope of strategic possibilities for my division. I had not expected that—they learn, I learn."

"The problem is you!" she kidded.

"Ah, you'll never let me forget that, will you?" he laughed good-naturedly. "But yes, the problem is me. My ability to get outstanding results is limited by my capacity to learn, and one can only learn in the context of good relationships. Every one, every day!"

"Well, looking back," smiled Jane, "if I think of that day when you told me in no uncertain terms that I was the problem, this definitely has been my journey. I used to look at each workday with dread and be angry at everything and everyone. Now the company is growing faster than I could have imagined, and I know the only limit is my ability to grow the right talents and leadership fast enough. As you said, look forward with hope and back with pride."

EPILOGUE

"Best supplier award, congratulations!"

Well, Jane thought, she could cross off meeting the formidable Phil Jenkinson, Ward's CEO and mentor, from her bucket list—right after coming up with a better bucket list. She was seated next to him at a round banquet table, with an ungainly piece of crystal sculpture standing in front of her plate. He was not what she had imagined. A big man with coarse features and rimless glasses—taller than Ward even—younger than she'd expected. He showed up to the gala diner in a jean shirt and beige chinos (the invite had said smart casual), making her feel distinctly overdressed. He spoke slowly with a pronounced twang and she had to take care not to jump in every time he paused—she'd interrupted him twice already thinking he was finished with what he'd been saying. He certainly didn't conform to her mental image of the captain of industry. Still, Nexplas was constantly cited as an up-and-coming firm, both for the results it posted and its culture—whatever that word meant.

"And thank you for Andy's education, as well," he drawled on.

"Andy's education?" she chortled. "Surely the other way around."

"Ah. It goes both ways. I've been pushing him for years to tackle supplier development as his personal kaizen. Up to 70% of our costs are linked to purchased materials and components, so we can't succeed if we don't improve our working partnership with our suppliers. When he told me he'd started with a software provider, I admit I was a little surprised, not to say dubious. But I'm glad it worked out in the end."

Teaching her had been Ward's kaizen project, she realized, slightly flummoxed.

"We're very happy with the work you've been doing for us here. We have so many IT issues. Have you considered opening a branch stateside?"

She shook her head, gathering her thoughts.

"We've been growing rapidly," she answered cautiously. "It's a risk in itself."

"Agreed. But please think about it. I've been talking this over with Andy, and we would like to share your work with the rest of our worldwide operations."

"Thank you, we'd love to do it."

"You've earned it."

"I owe a lot to Andy's advice."

"Words are cheap," Phil laughed. "Doing it is hard, that's what counts."

"The practice, right?" she grinned.

"The practice," he agreed.

"And there is nothing more than that?" she wondered out loud. "No greater vision? One thing I treasure about your approach is that it's really people-centric. We're putting humans back at the center of things. But Andy is always very reluctant to discuss general terms."

"He is incredibly pragmatic; it's his greatest strength," noted Phil thoughtfully. "And as so often, it can also be a flaw ..." his voice trailed off. He suddenly fixed his eyes on Jane.

"Are you asking me if there's more to leading with respect?"

"I guess so," she said, suddenly wondering what she'd gotten into, as she realized that he was taking her question seriously.

"It's a big, fast world out there," he finally answered. "So although I don't think there are any large answers, I do believe in asking large questions." She noticed that he carried with him a battered notebook, worn from years of use and with loose papers falling out. He looked at it briefly, seeming to consider looking something up, then gathered his thoughts and spoke.

"Here's the thing: The leap of faith I had to make was that spending a large part of my time on the shop floor encouraging people to solve safety, quality, flexibility, and productivity problems, day in day out, would radically transform my company. And as I stuck with it I came to realize that it really did. The large questions I was asking myself about strategy, organization, and systems became more focused, more specific.

"In essence, I see this not as a leap of faith, but a leap of practice. Often, I reframe my large challenges according to something I've experienced at a customer site or discussing a countermeasure with operators and frontline management. This is how I came to understand that lean is the key strategy. Kaizen and involving every one in kaizen is the compass that allows me to reconcile the need for changing the business at large and self-actualization of its people. It's a pretty large thought, I think," he said with a slow smile.

"I'd put it like this," he continued. "I believe we have a societal project—we benefit society by making things with minimum waste. The bigger question is why would customers buy our products?

"Then we have a social project—we believe in making people before making things. So why would the best and the brightest want to work for us?

"Finally, I think we have a managerial project, which is about looking for specific answers at the shop floor, where value is being created by engaging and involving all our employees through kaizen. So how can we increase value-added activity and minimize waste?"

"Which is what makes you profitable?"

"To a large extent, yes. We share a kernel of costs with all our competitors. Material prices are what they are, labor costs at any location are common to all, and so on. But the operational method one uses adds another layer of created costs to this basic nut. We're constantly looking for a productive frontier, if you will. So we constantly kaizen to get closer to the nut. But don't get me wrong, our profitability comes from making products customers buy."

"Seeking the productivity frontier, that's a great description. I really struggled with this at first," Jane confessed. "I found it hard, this notion of exploration without a clear destination in sight when we set out."

"We learn by doing."

"I can see it now, with hindsight. But it's not like a project where you have a clear objective, and understand what the steps are, and the expectations for improvement."

"No," he agreed. "It's a management method, not a productivity project. And it all starts with being there, where value happens, and supporting kaizen and respect."

"My main challenge," Jenkinson continued after another longish pause, "is to develop more leaders, not more followers. The irony is that the one sure way I've found to do this is to get people to spend more time on the shop floor, discussing what they see, sharing what they understand about their problems, and talking about what they intend to do."

"Observation and confirmation."

"Hours of discussion on the shop floor," he chuckled. "With a mentor or a coach. It's what I call helicopter thinking—the process of zooming in and out on details, learning to shift constantly from the technical details of any situation to the big picture and back."

"If I may ask: are you still coached?"

"Sure am. By a crotchedy guy named Bob Woods, the same sensei who helped me turn around my first business a decade ago. And he still makes me feel like I'm an idiot most of the time. But I've learned my lesson, and have several coaches now according to what I'm trying to learn. One of the difficulties, you'll see, is to keep the spirit of inquiry and improvement alive."

"If you've had enough of shop-floor visits, it's time to sell the company," she joked.

"Did Andy tell you that?" he grinned. "I say it all the time."

"I think I'm beginning to share the sentiment. It's amazing what I keep learning at customers' operations, or with my own teams."

"Then you're getting it. *Lead with respect.* At the end of the day, this is the core attitude. The rest is technique. But there's more to it than learning for yourself. It's a leadership-development practice—for others and for you. It does start with self-development. I usually do it by grabbing one of my guys and asking him or her to kaizen an area I need to understand better. I don't expect them to solve the problem, but I've grown confident that we'll all understand it better, which helps me to better frame the questions and set a direction.

"Then you coach others, as I've tried to coach Andy, and he's coached you. The question is: who are you coaching?

"You also need to keep clarifying the direction and keep chipping at it time and time again. We can confirm which challenges we need to solve today, and that will open space for growth for tomorrow. Then you support the kaizen spirit—every day, everywhere, all people all the time. And as you do this, you see things change for the better and the company transform itself. But the moment you stop, it all reverses back to where it was."

"I'm finding this out for sure," Jane said. "And it works, no question. But do you enjoy it?" she asked, surprising herself by asking such a direct, personal question.

"I do enjoy it, actually," he smiled, looking younger still as he did. "It's hard work, of course—particularly at first, but it does get easier as you go. So yes, I do enjoy it. The constant challenge keeps the job interesting, which to me is the most important thing if you're going to break your back and travel around the world nonstop. I'm not bored a single day. I always loved engineering and there's not one day that I don't have the chance to look into really interesting problems. And it's a real thrill every time we make customers happy with a clever solution that both pleases them and reduces our manufacturing cost. Then I believe we really *get it*—and it's great. I continue to find this fun.

"Also, I enjoy the success, let's be honest about it. When I first discovered lead with respect I was failing as a CEO. Since then, I've never looked back and, knock on wood, we've been far more successful than I ever imagined. And beyond the personal high, there is nothing like sharing success to make relationships easier. Being a CEO used to be something I had to do to develop my technical ideas. But now it's become a real calling. It makes a difference.

"And last but not least, I get a real kick at discovering people. They surprise me every day. I've learned I can't ever take anyone at face value. Look at Andy," he chuckled. "The first time I met him I thought I'd have to let him go, and look at where he is now! On the other side, a few people I thought were stars had to leave the company because they couldn't listen or learn. But it's wonderful to see what people who can learn individually can achieve when they team up.

"As a whole, I think we've put together a good group of people who are constantly learning to work with each other. And this is enjoyable. There is also a tremendous amount of pride when you're in a plant in China and the local group leader encourages an operator to demonstrate the clever idea she just had, and you realize that you need to get your engineers to understand what she's doing because it's going to make the product better. This is absolutely, no-doubt-about-it, a ball."

––––––––––

"Everything good?" asked Ward, as she caught up with him to say goodbye. He was chatting to Jenkinson and looking stiff in his formal three-piece suit.

"Excellent," she answered, smiling. "Or is that the wrong thing to say? The worst problem is no problem, is that it?"

Jenkinson chuckled amicably, looking at Ward with raised brows.

"Speak for yourself," Ward sighed. "I've had my arms full with problems of every kind just putting this supplier event together. I hate these corporate to-dos! I'm not good at the shaking hands and kissing babies part of the job. The U.S. has been doing these for years, so I've finally come around to it, as well. 'Copy and improve,'" he sniggered, hovering between self-deprecation and being pleased with himself.

"Yeah. Well, it's a success," she said. "And thank you.

"And thank you," she said turning to Jenkinson, "for offering to find us work in the States—and for your insights. I can see I still have much to learn about leading with respect."

"The biggest room is the room for improvement," the big man answered jokingly. "You're doing well, very well. We could really use your help with our stateside IT, seriously. And you asked some good questions—I'm still mulling them over. What is the key? Is it fun? Is the true spirit of respect tapping into the fun of creation? … Well, much to think about … Goodnight."

———————

It was the next morning, and Delaney watched Jenkinson and Ward whispering intensely to each other in the midst of Southcape's open floor. Phil had asked if he could see her gemba before taking his flight out and Andy came along. She couldn't help but notice how different today's visit felt than the first time Andy was there.

As she took a step back, trying to see her workplace through their eyes, she felt immensely proud of how much progress they had made. The open space was quiet in a busy way, with team spaces clearly visible, coders having organized their own areas as they liked with a few common reference points, such as a large visible project plan, a daily problem-solving paperboard, and whatever key info they felt necessary on the wall. She just knew what Andy would say: too many papers on the walls spoil the line of sight, people need to look up and see success conditions, not be overburdened by too much clutter.

She was certainly enjoying the sight of him being coached. Phil had one of their A3s in hand and was listening in such a way that she could clearly see Andy was justifying—explaining—something or other. It was definitely a guilty pleasure to see the shoe on the other foot for a change.

Yes, she was proud of her teams. Phil had toured the offices and she noticed the easygoing hellos from the developers who greeted him without looking askance or breaking their stride. He had been very quiet, just looking, asking a few questions.

She realized that she didn't mind this visit. She felt no pressure at all, no fear that having him at her company would expose any weaknesses she wanted hidden. She thought about how this small moment of observation was indeed the kernel, the basis of all the systemic, cultural, "big" changes that had taken place at Nexplas—and were beginning to change her own company. It also struck her how satisfying it felt at that moment to be doing this work right now with both of them. There was an odd a kind of comradeship in just standing there and watching with someone—when you take the time to really look and to listen.

———————

"Seven theories, Andy. Seven, no less," Phil was saying as she came closer to find out what the debate was all about.

"Seven what?" she asked.

"Seven theories on everything," Andy sighed. "Phil is right. In doing A3 problem solving, we expect to see at least seven hypotheses outlined, each with their specific confirmation method."

"Why seven?"

"It's an insight my sensei taught me," Phil explained. "Three theories are easy to think of. When you ask for number four and five, people start cheating, phrasing differently their existing beliefs, what they already know. To get to the seventh, they have to force themselves out of what they know and into creative thinking. Then they start looking at the problem with fresh eyes."

"Right …"

"Andy's been working with you on observation and confirmation, and you both have done an excellent job. But keeping an open mind is just as important. Creative thinking comes from divergent thinking: the ability to look at any situation in different ways and accept that each could be valid. There never is a single story.

"What we're really doing is giving people space to think and encouraging creative thinking. We need to both open minds and develop judgment through confirmation. It's basic scientific thinking. You start with intuition, then you experiment and count cases where your intuition works—and more importantly where it doesn't—until you rephrase a more likely hypothesis, and so on. The convergence through confirmation is essential. But you must first open minds to make space for creative intuition."

"I see …" said Jane thoughtfully, not seeing at all, but amused at how every door opened yet another door seemingly endlessly.

"I was arguing that you were doing great work on confirmation already," chipped in Andy, "and to let you get used to this before introducing yet another paradox."

"Do it right from the start," Phil said, smiling, "and people will surprise you."

"In resisting, yeah," grumbled Andy.

"Actually, I've thought about that," Jane ventured. "I've thought about the learning process that we went through—me and my teams. We seem to go through a cycle of excitement, then discouragement, and finally fun."

"How do you mean?" asked Phil.

"I'm not sure how to explain it. But look, every time we tackle a new topic, we're curious at first. We think about it, we figure out a way to go forward, and so on. Next, it gets bloody uncomfortable as we hit the first obstacles and things don't go the way we'd hoped. The challenge is not to get discouraged along the way. Then we finally get the hang of whatever we were trying to do and it becomes fun!

"And then we move on to the next thing," she continued. "I've been watching how different people work different ways. Some go through phases of interest, then get discouraged with the discomfort of the learning phase, abandon it, and get interested in something else. Some get obsessed with what they've learned once they've passed the distress zone, but keep tinkering with their new toy without picking up a new interest. Some enjoy the challenge of breaking through the walls they encounter. And so on.

"This is how I try to steer them: new topic, time to think, see how we can do something, be ready to hit snags and feel we'll never succeed, commit not to give up, and finally enjoying success. As you said, the joy of creation."

"Curiosity, tension, fun," Phil reformulated, carefully writing it down in his battered notebook. "Thank you for that, Jane. This is very insightful. We know that without some degree of stress in solving problems, people don't care enough to be bothered to try, and if there's too much stress they panic and freeze. But I had not thought of before and after. I think you're right. More fun would make it easier to get people on board."

"The problem, if I may," Jane volleyed, "is that the focus on learning by problem solving keeps people constantly in the tension zone, but there's not much for either curiosity or fun. This is what I guess you were addressing with the seven theories, trying to encourage curiosity, right? After all, the challenge is to find a way for them to care."

The two men just stared at each other until Andy suddenly laughed out aloud.

"You know what, you've got us pegged!" he grinned. "Damn, you're good. I know how to keep people learning, but am always at a loss at how to get them interested in the first place or enjoy the process. Well, I guess we have our kaizen topic laid out for us!"

Jane allowed herself a short moment of genuine satisfaction in having showed them for a change. As she thought about it after they had left, she realized with a start that it hadn't been a 'being right' moment, but rather the unique experience of the kind of intense collaboration she'd previously discussed with Andy. Last night's award didn't matter to her as much as the way she felt that she had graduated. She'd kicked a key question around with two people she respected and they'd listened—and she knew they would come up with something good in return. Now, this was fun!

There is a particular peace that comes when you realize that the larger problems are in your mind—when you realize that there are only a string of small problems that you can solve one after another. That you don't need to think yourself out of the situation; but that you can do both the thinking and the doing. Try and go see, try and go see; only the next step matters; then the next.

In the heart of the question, in the space of doing, there is a special moment. If you catch it, if you learn to really listen, you can help others say something new—something that you can then say, 'Yes, we will do it as you say, and we will do it now.' In that moment, your workers are as much part of the company as you are. You suddenly let go of your obsession with doing something about them and realize you can enjoy doing something with them—and watch them grow. They are the pebbles that can start the avalanche that changes the direction of the entire journey. And if that doesn't happen in this moment, never mind.

Next week is a new beginning. For that matter, tomorrow is a new beginning. Right now is a new beginning.

ACKNOWLEDGMENTS

The characters and situations in this novel are entirely fictitious. Although we have based the story on our experiences at the frontline and the teachings of our sensei, the book does not pretend in any way to be a description of either the Toyota Production System (TPS) or the Toyota Way. References to TPS or Toyota way in the book reflect only our understanding of their application outside of Toyota and in no way claim to represent the position of the Toyota Motor Corp.

Heartfelt thanks to the book's chief editor Tom Ehrenfeld, who has, again, greatly contributed to the shaping of this book from its first draft to its current form—indeed, the writing of this book followed the path it describes, with Tom as a true sensei on the page!

In writing the story, we have relied on the experiences of many managers who do this every day at the gemba. More particularly, we owe a large debt to Mr. Nampachi Hayashi both for his shop-floor teachings of TPS and deep insights into lean management according to the Toyota Way.

In the use of these principles to transform the business culture, we have been fortunate to work with successful executives, such as Pierre Vareille, Jacques Chaize, Yves Mérel, Olivier Baldassari, Frédéric Fiancette, Evrard Guelton, Jean-Baptiste Bouthillon, Jean-Claude Bihr, Christophe Riboulet, Cyril Dané, Furio Clerico, Fabiano Clerico, Klaus Beulker, Norbert Dubost, Christophe Frachet, Catherine Blay, Patrick De Coster, Ariane Bouzette, Stéphane André, Hugues Pichon, François Papin, and many others.

Acknowledgments

Our gratitude also to our colleagues at the Institut Lean France for their support and advice, Marie-Pia Ignace, Cécile Roche, Catherine Chabiron, Godefroy Beauvallet, Benjamin Garel, Yves Caseau, Olivier Soulié, and Richard Kaminski.

On the IT front we would like to thank Emmanuel Chenu, Michael Kightley, Sandrine Olivencia, Florence Préault, Régis Médina, Antoine Contal, Paul Gette, Cécil Dijoux, Luc Robuschi, Jean-Baptise Degon, Daniel Breston, Phil Coy, and Pierre Masai for their insights, suggestions, corrections, and practical examples—all mistakes and misunderstandings are our own.

Thanks also to readers of the early versions of the book, Anne-Lise Seltzer and Stéphanie Frendo for their helpful feedback. Special thanks to Peter Handlinger and Trevor Graham for sharing their "the problem is you!" anecdotes while discussing "Ubuntu" (are you going to succeed personally in a way that makes the community around you improve) in Hluhluwe, which gives African roots to this book!

Many thanks also to Dan Jones for his constant support and inspiration and to Jim Womack for his thorough read, insightful, detailed comments, and writing the foreword. Thank you also to John Shook for his guidance. Thanks as well to many other leading experts who generously contributed their time, experience, and valuable inputs through conversations along the way, including Jeff Liker, Orest Fiume, Art Smalley, Tracey Richardson, Durward Sobek, David Meier, Mike Hoseus, Marcus Chao, René Aernoudts, Steve Bell, and Gilberto Kosaka.

Many thanks also to the Lean Enterprise Institute team involved in the production of the book for their dedication and hard work: Thomas Skehan, Jane Bulnes-Fowles, Chet Marchwinski, and to the reviewers who made many thoughtful comments.

Finally, we would like to thank our family for their support and patience as they've often had to sit through more lean talk than anyone in their right mind would want to.

INDEX

Index

Lean Enterprise Institute

Continue Your Learning

The Lean Enterprise Institute (LEI) has a wide range of learning resources, all with the practical knowledge you need to sustain a lean transformation:

Learning Materials

Our plain-language books, workbooks, leadership guides, and training materials reflect the essence of lean thinking—*doing*. They draw on years of research and real-world experiences from lean transformations in manufacturing and service organizations to provide tools that you can put to work immediately.

Education

Faculty members with extensive implementation experience teach you actual applications with the case studies, work sheets, formulas, and methodologies you need for implementation. Select from courses that address technical topics, culture change, coaching, senior management's roles, and much more.

Events

Every March the Lean Transformation Summit explores the latest lean concepts and case studies, presented by executives and implementers. Other events focus on an issue or industry, such as starting a lean transformation or implementing lean in healthcare. Check *lean.org* for details and to get first notice of these limited-attendance events.

lean.org

A quick and secure sign-up delivers these online learning resources:

- Thought-leading e-letters from lean experts delivered directly to your inbox.
- Access to the *A3 Dojo* where you can ask your A3 problem-solving questions and get help from LEI faculty.
- Use of the *Connection Center* to network or benchmark with fellow Lean Thinkers.
- Entry to a range of *Forums* where you can ask questions or help others.
- Access to the *Lean Road Map* for customizing and tracking a personal learning path.
- Use of the *Lean Notebook* for saving and sharing important articles.
- First notice about LEI events, webinars, and new learning materials.

About the Lean Enterprise Institute, Inc.

The Lean Enterprise Institute was founded in 1997 by management expert and author James P. Womack, Ph.D., as a nonprofit research, education, publishing, and conferencing company. As part of its mission to advance lean thinking around the world, LEI supports the Lean Global Network (leanglobal.org), the Lean Education Academic Network (teachinglean.org), and the Healthcare Value Network (createvalue.org/delivery/hvn).